Automotive Systems

Fuel, Lubrication, and Cooling

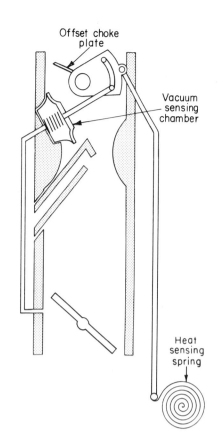

HERBERT E. ELLINGER

Associate Professor
Transportation Technology
Western Michigan University

Automotive Systems
Fuel, Lubrication, and Cooling

Prentice-Hall, Inc.
Englewood Cliffs, N.J.

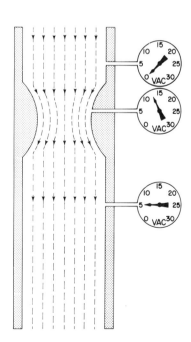

Library of Congress Cataloging in Publication Data

ELLINGER, HERBERT E.
 Automotive systems.

 Includes index.
  1. Automobiles—Motors—Maintenance and repair.
2. Motor vehicles—Pollution control devices—Maintenance and
repair. I. Title.
TL210.E37   629.2'5   75-8563
ISBN 0-13-055269-0

10 9 8 7 6 5 4 3 2 1

Printed in the United States of America

PRENTICE-HALL INTERNATIONAL, INC., London
PRENTICE-HALL OF AUSTRALIA, PTY. LTD., Sydney
PRENTICE-HALL OF CANADA, LTD., Toronto
PRENTICE-HALL OF INDIA PRIVATE LIMITED, New Delhi
PRENTICE-HALL OF JAPAN, INC., Tokyo

To My Students

whose constructive reactions
to my lectures and instructional methods
helped write this book

Contents

Contents

Preface

Legislation to control automotive emissions has resulted in complex automobile engine operating systems. When a component of one of the engine systems malfunctions the engine often operates poorly and this generally leads to a drivability problem, excessive emissions, or low gas mileage. Most of the emission control systems involve devices that modify the operation of the fuel system, ignition system, and cooling system. This increases operational demands on the engine lubrication system and on the engine electrical system.

The engine manufacturers' have designed emission controlled engines to meet federal emission regulations. Maintaining these engines at the proper emission level is accomplished by the technician as he performs an engine tune-up. This tune-up is more involved than a tune-up of a non-emission controlled engine.

The technician must be skilled to properly maintain the modern emission controlled engine to provide minimum emissions with satisfactory drivability and gasoline mileage. In the first place he needs to understand the basic operating principles of the engine systems. In addition, he needs to know how the emission control devices are used to modify the engine systems and operating characteristics. To maintain these systems the technician needs to know how to test the operation of the engine systems and their component parts and how to make the required adjustments.

Different automobile engine manufacturers have taken various approaches to control emissions. Each engine model is considered separately by the Environmental Protection Agency, and so each is modified and equipped with only the specific items necessary to make it meet Federal Emission Standards. Therefore, almost every engine–vehicle combination is equipped with different control systems. In this book the engine systems have been summarized by their functions and how they help to control emissions. Essentially, emission controls work in three ways: carefully conditioning the induction charge, controlling combustion of the charge in the engine, and reducing harmful emissions in the exhaust gases. Each function is described in detail.

Some of the emission control devices, such as the PCV system, air preheat, and evaporative control system, do not detract from engine performance. Emission controls that are used to modify the combustion process generally reduce the engine's thermal efficiency and therefore reduce the gasoline mileage. This is in direct opposition to conservation of energy and good gasoline mileage, but it is necessary to meet emission standards when using the engine modification method of emission control.

During the time the manuscript for this book was being prepared both Federal Emission Standards and the means of controlling vehicle emissions were being constantly modified. The information has been updated as much as possible until publication prevented further revision. The reader should keep in mind that some information contained in this book has probably been modified before publication.

Federal Emission Standards only apply to the automobile manufacturers and to their dealers. Some state laws and municipal ordinances apply to the automobile service technician and to the automobile operator. These standards differ from one other and from the federal standards. I have reviewed all standards available to me; therefore the maximum emission test values given in this book will meet or be below any local emission standards.

Test and diagnosis procedures differ between those of the automobile manufacturer and those of the test equipment manufacturer. The automobile manufacturer's test procedures are keyed to the type of equipment they require their dealers to have. Equipment manufacturers, on the other hand, have devised pieces of test equipment that can be used to test the vehicle's operating systems very rapidly and thus save the technician time on these jobs. This allows the technician additional time to do additional jobs on the same day, enabling him to increase his income. The most common test procedures are presented in this book. Some manufacturers have test procedures that are somewhat different from those described. It is always advisable to review the manufacturer's service manual for special procedures before making unfamiliar tests or while working on unfamiliar automobiles.

The objective of this book is to present adequate information so that the reader will be able, with practice in following the procedures presented, to properly test, diagnose, repair, and tune-up an emission controlled engine. It would be helpful if the reader thoroughly understood automotive electricity; however, enough information on electrical systems is provided so that the reader can identify problems in the electrical system. Details on electrical system repairs have been limited to the ignition contact points, condenser, spark plugs, and ignition timing. These electrical components have a direct bearing on engine operation and engine emissions.

Most of the text is devoted to carburetion, fuel systems, emission control, and details of the tune-up procedures used on modern engines. Lubricating and cooling systems are included because they require routine maintenance and they have an effect on vehicle emissions.

I want to express sincere thanks to all those who have helped make this book possible. Special thanks must go to the automobile manufacturers and equipment companies that provided many excellent illustrations. They are listed in the Acknowledgements. Thanks should also go to Steve Weaver who spent many hours preparing photographs and to Gerald Helsley who was very helpful in correcting early drafts. The unrestricted use of the Automotive Laboratories, automotive equipment, and the training aids at Western Michigan University is especially appreciated. Help was received from the automotive teaching staff and automotive students who brought new and unusual items to my attention for inclusion in this book. Many thanks are given to Gertrude Lamoreaux and Linda Campbell for typing the manuscript, and recognition must be given to my wife Christine, without whose encouragement this book could not have been written.

HERBERT E. ELLINGER

Acknowledgements

A great number of individuals and organizations have cooperated in providing reference material and illustrations used in this text. The author wishes to express sincere thanks to the following organizations for their special contributions:

Allen Test Products
American Motors Company
Beckman Instruments Incorporated
Carter Carburetor Company
Champion Spark Plug Company
Chrysler Motors Corporation
Ford Motor Company
General Motors Corporation
   AC Spark Plug Division
   Buick Motor Division
   Cadillac Motor Car Division
   Delco Remy Division
   GM Research Division
   Rochester Products Division
   Oldsmobile Division
Holley Carburetor Company
Kal-Equip Company
Marquette Corporation
Modine Manufacturing Company
The Prestolite Company
Society of Automotive Engineers
Society for Testing Materials
Sun Electric Corporation

Automotive Systems

Fuel, Lubrication, and Cooling

1

Engine Operation

Vehicle movement depends upon the power produced by the engine. The engine converts part of the energy of the fuel into useful power. Fuel is mixed with air in the proper proportions by the carburetor or fuel-injection system to make the intake charge. This air/fuel charge is drawn through an intake manifold and an intake valve to fill the combustion chamber, then the valve closes. The charge is compressed and ignited at the precise instant required. After ignition the charge will burn very rapidly. Combustion in the engine is so fast it is usually called an explosion but if the engine is to function properly the charge burning must be controlled. Controlled burning, called combustion, releases the fuel energy in the form of heat. The resulting heat increases the pressure of the gases within the cylinder combustion chamber. In a typical reciprocating engine the high pressure forces a piston to move down in its cylinder. Piston movement is transferred to a rotating crankshaft through a connecting rod. When the piston approaches the bottom of its downward stroke an exhaust valve opens, releasing the expanded combustion gases into an exhaust manifold and muffler system. The sequence then repeats itself.

Small utility engines usually have only one cylinder. As more power is needed more cylinders are used, with their combustion cycles alternating to provide smooth power output. Automobiles using reciprocating engines with pistons moving up and down in the cylinder either have four or six in-line cylinders, or have two banks of three or four cylinders each within a common block and using a common crankshaft that forms a V-six or V-eight engine.

The basic engine needs several auxiliary systems in order to function. It requires a fuel system to transfer fuel from the tank to the carburetor or fuel injector; an ignition system is required to supply an arc across spark plug electrodes at the correct instant in each cylinder. A cooling system is also required to keep engine heat under control. Moving parts are kept from touching by a cushion of oil supplied by the engine's lubricating system. Failure of any of these systems will cause engine failure.

1-1 ENGINE CYCLES

Engine cycles are identified by the number of piston *strokes* required to complete the cycle. A piston stroke is a one-way piston movement between top and bottom of the cylinder. Most automobile engines use a four-stroke cycle.

The *four-stroke cycle* starts with the piston at the top of the stroke with the piston close to the head. An intake valve opens as the piston moves down on the first, or *intake stroke*, allowing the combustible charge to enter the cylinder. The intake valve closes after the bottom of the stroke, and as the crankshaft continues to rotate the piston

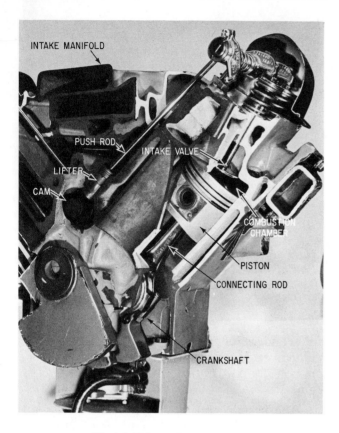

Fig. 1-1 Major engine components.

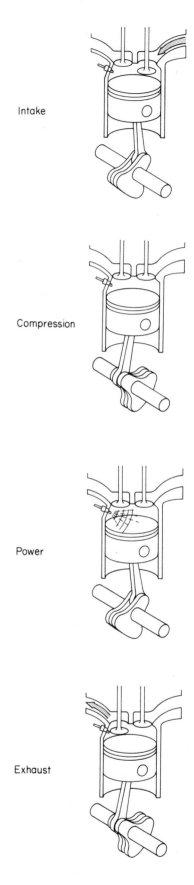

Intake

Compression

Power

Exhaust

Fig. 1-2 Typical four-stroke engine cycle.

moves up on the second stroke, or *compression stroke*, to squeeze the charge into a small space called the *combustion chamber*. Near the top of the compression stroke, the spark plug ignites the compressed charge so the fuel will burn. The heat released raises the charge pressure and the pressure pushes the piston down on the third, or *power stroke*. Near the bottom of the stroke, the exhaust valve opens to release the spent exhaust gases as the piston moves up on the fourth, or *exhaust stroke* to complete a 720-degree four-stroke cycle. The piston is then in a position to start the next cycle with another intake stroke. The four-stroke cycle is repeated every other crankshaft revolution.

Some engines use a *two-stroke cycle*. This cycle starts with piston at top center on the power stroke. As the piston nears the bottom of the power stroke, the exhaust opens to release the spent gases. The intake opens very shortly after the exhaust opens and a charge is forced into the cylinder. This aids in pushing the exhaust gases from the cylinder. Both valves or ports close as the piston starts up on the compression stroke. The two-stroke cycle engine has a power stroke each crankshaft revolution. Two-stroke cycles are used in some small gasoline engines and in some diesel engines.

1-2 IGNITION SYSTEM

An air/fuel charge, compression, and ignition are required to make an engine start and run. Of the three, ignition is most critical. The correct amount of fuel mixed with the air is required for proper engine operation; however, the engine will start, even with no carburetor, if a small amount of gasoline is poured into the intake manifold. High compression is required for maximum power and economy but the engine will start and run with low compression. In all cases the ignition system must be able to produce a strong enough spark at the correct instant to ignite the air/fuel mixture after it has been compressed in the cylinder.

Ignition requirements change as engine operating conditions change. Higher compression pressures require higher ignition voltage, a term given to electrical pressure. Cold combustion chambers require higher ignition voltages while starting than do warmed-up chambers. Both rich and lean air/fuel mixtures require higher ignition voltages than the chemically correct mixtures. For proper combustion that leads to engine efficiency, the ignition timing must advance as engine speed increases. Part throttle operation requires more ignition advance than does full throttle operation or idle. Exhaust emission is affected by ignition timing and so the function of some emission controls is to change ignition timing to minimize polluting exhaust emissions. These changes usually reduce the thermal efficiency of the engine and reduce the gas mileage.

The ignition system must provide a voltage that is high enough to form an arc between the

spark plug electrodes at the correct instant in the engine cycle that will allow the engine to produce the required power, economy, and emission level demanded of modern automobile engines.

The ignition system consists of two parts: a low-voltage *primary* circuit and a high-voltage *secondary* circuit. The primary circuit includes the battery, ignition switch, ballast resistor, cam-operated breaker points, condenser, and the heavy primary windings in the coil with their connecting wiring. The secondary circuit includes the large number of fine coil secondary windings, the distributor rotor, distributor cap, ignition cables, and spark plugs.

When the ignition switch and breaker points are closed in a typical ignition system the primary circuit is completed, through ground, to allow electrical current to flow in the primary circuit. This current flow builds a magnetic field in the coil. As the engine rotates it turns the breaker-point cam within the distributor housing. The cam pushes against the breaker-point rubbing block, forcing the points apart. Breaker-point separation interrupts and stops the primary current flow. When the current flow stops, the magnetic field in the coil collapses through the secondary windings. The condenser within the distributor minimizes contact point arcing as it helps control the rapid collapse of the magnetic field. Field collapse induces a momentary high voltage surge in the coil secondary windings. At this instant the rotor tip is lined up with the proper distributor cap electrode. The high voltage is impressed through the secondary cables on the spark plug in the cylinder to be fired, causing an arc to form across the spark plug gap. This arc ignites the compressed air/fuel charge in the com-

Fig. 1-3 Schematic of a typical standard ignition system.

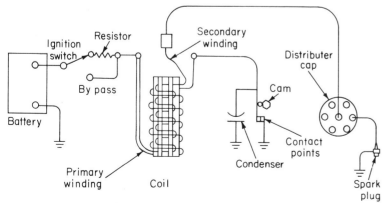

bustion chamber at the correct instant. The resulting combustion increases pressure above the piston to push it down in the cylinder.

1-3 IGNITION TIMING

No matter what type of ignition system is used—it may be a conventional design, it may use transistor switching, or it may use a capacitive discharge system—the spark must be delivered to the spark plug with enough energy to ignite the charge.

It is not only important for the charge to ignite, but it must ignite at the correct instant so that the burning charge will produce maximum useful energy as the hot gases expand within the combustion chamber. The spark arc is timed so that maximum combustion chamber pressure occurs when the crank pin is 5° to 10° after top center. The ignition firing or timing point needs to be adjusted during engine operation for changes in the charge that affect burning rates so that maximum pressure will always occur at 5° to 10° after top center under all operating conditions requiring engine power.

Ignition Timing and Engine Speed. The first 10% of the combustion charge burns at a constant rate; that is, it takes a specific length of time to

burn, no matter what the engine speed happens to be. To compensate for this, a mechanical timing mechanism is used to advance the ignition firing point as engine speed increases.

After the first 10% of the charge has burned the combustion rate increase is proportional to engine speed. This is primarily the result of increased turbulence in the combustion chamber created by a high velocity intake charge, combustion chamber squash area (the narrow space between the piston and head at top center), and flame turbulence. Without this characteristic, engines could not run at high speeds as required in racing. At some high rpm, depending on the engine design, the first 10% becomes insignificant so that no further ignition advance is required.

Ignition Timing and Engine Load. The mass or weight of the charge that is taken into the combustion chamber, as the result of throttle position and engine load, also affects timing requirements. Under light throttle operation, high manifold vacuum occurs and a *small quantity* of charge is drawn into the combustion chamber. Pressure resulting from compression of this small charge is low and its burning rate is slow. This low pressure type of charge requires high ignition advance to complete combustion at 5° to 10° after top center. At these low compression pressures, the spark plug arc will form at a low required voltage.

During low-speed, full-throttle engine operation, a *large quantity* of charge enters the combustion chamber because the open throttle provides minimum intake restriction. When compressed, this large charge is dense and has high pressure. More gas molecules are present between the spark plug electrodes, increasing the electrical resistance and thus increasing the voltage required. Once kindled, combustion occurs quite rapidly through the dense mixture so timing is retarded to have combustion complete at 5° to 10° after top center.

Ignition timing could be compared to going to a drag race. If the race began at six o'clock, one would plan to start early enough to arrive on time. His starting time would depend on the road type, the traffic anticipated, and the weather. The ignition system is designed to anticipate the expected length of time to complete combustion; then it must start early enough in the cycle so that combustion is completed at the correct time.

A vacuum timing-advance mechanism is used to change ignition timing to compensate for throttle position and engine load. Timing is *advanced* under high intake manifold vacuum, light load operation when the burning rate is slow. It is *retarded* under

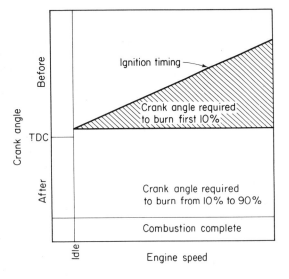

Fig. 1-4 Combustion burning rate in terms of engine speed and degrees of crankshaft rotation.

low intake manifold vacuum, heavy load operation when fast burning rates occur. The vacuum advance is fully retarded at full throttle because it is not required for maximum engine power. The primary function of the vacuum advance is to provide fuel economy during part throttle operation by igniting the charge at an advance that will give maximum effective combustion pressure at the engine operating conditions. Restricting vacuum advance is one of the major methods used to control exhaust hydrocarbons.

Ignition Timing and Emissions. The emission quality is greatly affected by the timing of the instant that the charge is ignited in the engine cycle. The maximum amount of fuel energy is transformed into useful work when combustion is most efficient. This leaves less heat to be exhausted and so the exhaust gases are at a lower temperature. The exhaust gases from an efficiently operating engine, however, contain excessive hydrocarbons and carbon monoxide when the engine runs rich with the throttle closed, at idle and especially during deceleration. By retarding the timing, engine efficiency is reduced so the throttle must be opened further to maintain the same speed. The mixture can be leaned when using a larger throttle opening. These conditions result in higher engine exhaust operating temperatures. Increased exhaust heat helps to complete the combustion of hydrocarbons and carbon monoxide as the spent gases flow through the exhaust system. Rapid distributor advance as the engine comes up to power gives the engine normal ignition advance for economy cruise and for high speed operation.

To make sure that the vacuum does not cause the ignition to advance during acceleration some manufacturers have a transmission spark control

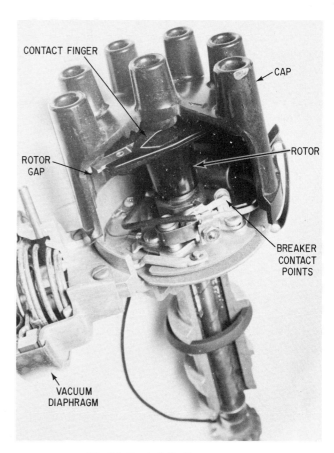

Fig. 1-6 Typical distributor parts.

(TSC) system connected to the transmission to allow vacuum advance in direct drive only.

During deceleration the engine has a high intake manifold vacuum. If the throttle were only partly closed during deceleration the distributor vacuum port in the carburetor would be exposed to manifold vacuum. This would cause the vacuum to advance the distributor timing and produce more hydrocarbons and carbon monoxide. Some automatic-transmission-equipped engines are fitted with a modified distributor advance unit connected to special carburetor ports to insure full ignition retard during deceleration. They may also have an electric solenoid attached to the vacuum-advance control unit. The purpose of the solenoid is to advance the ignition timing during engine cranking to assure quick and easy starting. The timing advance solenoid is only activated during cranking.

In some standard transmission vehicles lower hydrocarbon and carbon monoxide emissions will

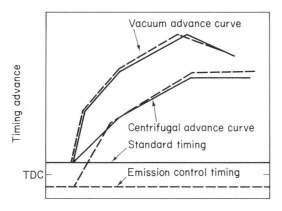

Fig. 1-5 Typical change in the distributor advance curve to reduce HC and CO exhaust emissions during low engine speed.

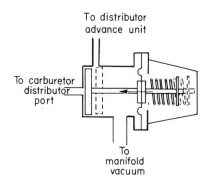

Fig. 1-7 Section drawing of a vacuum control valve used with some standard transmission engines.

be produced if the ignition timing is advanced during deceleration. This is accomplished by using a vacuum-controlled valve in the distributor vacuum hose. With the throttle closed the normal distributor vacuum port in the carburetor is open above the throttle plate where it is exposed to the atmosphere and so it provides no vacuum advance. Under these conditions the vacuum-controlled emission valve connects the distributor diaphragm to the engine manifold to give maximum vacuum advance which provides a longer period of time for combustion to take place within the combustion chamber before the exhaust valve opens.

REVIEW QUESTIONS

1. How does a two-stroke cycle differ from a four-stroke cycle?

2. Name the strokes of a four-stroke cycle.

3. When should maximum pressure occur in a combustion cycle?

4. What part of combustion requires a specific time period to complete?

5. What part of combustion is proportional to engine speed?

6. What distributor advance mechanism is sensitive to the load on the engine?

7. What distributor advance mechanism provides fuel economy?

8. How does timing affect hydrocarbon and carbon monoxide emissions?

2

Engine Electrical Systems

The lead-acid type battery is the primary source of electricity for starting modern engines. It also serves as a reserve source of electricity for the electrical running load of the vehicle. The battery size selected depends on the use to which it will be subjected. Vehicles with large engines require a greater cranking power and so a large battery is used. Large batteries are also used in vehicles with a number of electrically operated accessories. Small batteries are found in vehicles with small engines and light electrical loads.

A properly maintained lead-acid battery of the type used in automobiles will give from three to four years of trouble-free service. Proper maintenance involves keeping the battery clean, charged, full of water, and well-supported in the battery case. When a battery fails to start the engine, the technician must be able to check the battery and the rest of the electrical system to determine the cause of failure in order to properly correct the problem. It could be that the battery has failed or it could be that other electrical system parts have failed.

2-1 BATTERY CARE

In order to start an engine the battery must be in good condition to provide electrical power for cranking the engine and for ignition. To ensure dependable service the battery must be serviced during each tune-up, and sometimes more frequently.

During a tune-up the first considerations in checking a battery are its physical condition and its installation. The battery should be clean and should be securely mounted in a carrier with proper hold-down clamps. The cables must be clean and

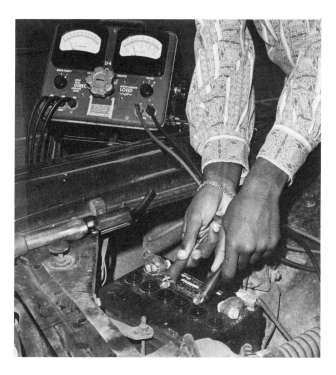

Fig. 2-1 Electricity bleeding across the battery top as shown on the voltmeter whose leads are touching the cover, not the battery posts.

7

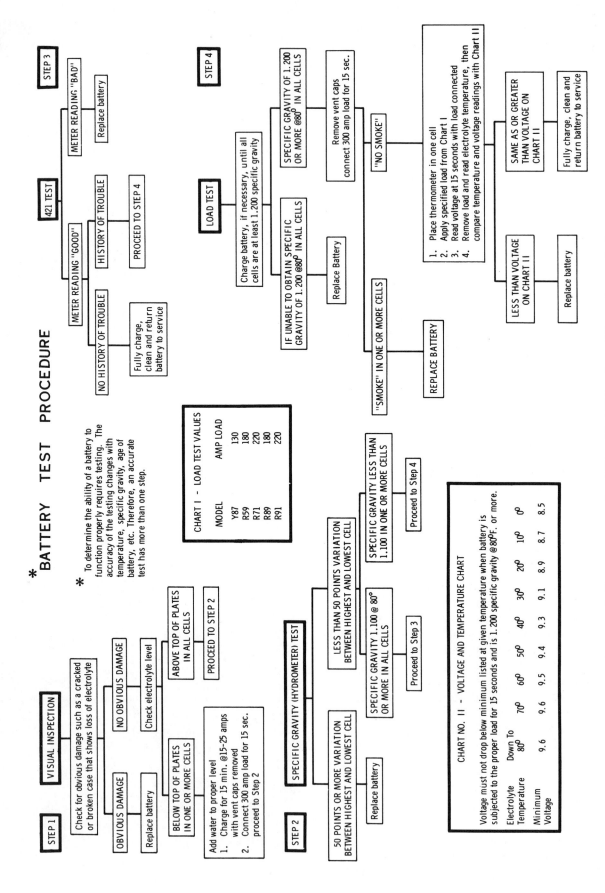

Fig. 2-2 Typical battery test procedure (Oldsmobile Division, General Motors Corporation).

tight. Pure water should be added to the battery electrolyte, to fill it to the indicator level. In many service stations, the battery electrolyte level is checked each time the engine oil level is checked. Only distilled water is recommended for addition to the electrolyte. In some areas drinking water has been satisfactorily used for battery water, but it is not recommended by battery manufacturers.

If the exterior of the battery is moist and dirty, electricity will bleed across the battery case between the battery posts on which the cables are attached. This will gradually discharge the battery. Leakage can easily be determined by placing voltmeter lead terminals in the moisture on the top of the battery. If leakage is occurring a voltage reading will be observed on the voltmeter.

2-2 BATTERY TESTING

Batteries should be tested to help prevent vehicle problems that result from battery failure. The battery is tested to determine its state-of-charge and how well it either produces or accepts current. The voltage a battery produces is tested while a known current flows. If the voltage of a fully charged battery is low while discharging or if it is either too high or too low while charging, the battery is faulty.

State-Of-Charge. As electricity is drawn from the battery the chemical reaction reduces the acidity of the electrolyte. This causes the electrolyte to thin or reduce its specific gravity. Specific gravity is measured with a *hydrometer*. If the specific gravity is high the electrolyte is thick and the hydrometer will float high. If the specific gravity is low the electrolyte is thin and the hydrometer floats low. The acid concentration in the electrolyte, as indicated by the hydrometer float level, is an indication of the battery *state-of-charge*.

A fully charged battery will have a hydrometer reading of 1260 (indicating a specific gravity 1.26 times that of water). A completely discharged battery will have a hydrometer reading of 1070 (indicating a specific gravity 1.07 times that of water). The use of a hydrometer is the best means of checking a battery state-of-charge. Two precautions should be considered when using a hydrometer. If water has just been added to the cell electrolyte it will remain on top of the plates. This will produce a hydrometer reading that is lower than the actual battery state-of-charge. The second precaution has to do with battery temperature. If

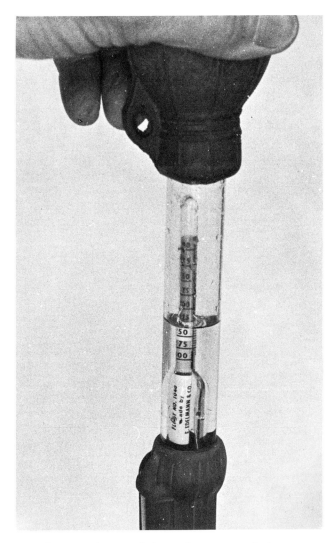

Fig. 2-3 Hydrometer being used to measure the battery state-of-charge.

the battery is hot the electrolyte will be thin and the hydrometer will give a false low reading. If the battery is cold the electrolyte will be thick and give the hydrometer a false high reading. Four points are added to the hydrometer reading for each 10°F (5.5°C) that the electrolyte temperature is above 80°F (27°C) and four points are subtracted for each 10°F (5.5°C) the electrolyte temperature is below 80°F (27°C). Good quality battery hydrometers have thermometers built into them with the correction factors indicated on the thermometer scale. Cells should be within 50 points on a good battery.

Capacity. The capacity test or load test measures the ability of the battery to rapidly convert chemical energy to electrical energy. This is done by drawing a heavy current from the battery while observing the terminal voltage at the battery posts. When current is drawn from the battery faster than the chemical action can occur within the battery, the battery terminal voltage is lowered. In the battery capacity test an *open* variable carbon pile resistor is connected in series with the fully charged battery and with an ammeter that can carry a large current, to complete an electrical circuit across the battery. The ammeter and carbon pile are usually contained within a battery-starter test unit. A voltmeter is also connected across the battery posts or terminals. The voltmeter is also part of a battery-starter tester. Voltage is noted 15 seconds after the carbon pile is adjusted to produce a current that is three times the ampere-hour capacity of the battery. Ampere-hour capacity is a rating used to indicate the maximum electrical potential power or size of the battery and is marked either on the battery or in specification books. For a healthy full-charged battery at 80°F (27°C) or above, the battery terminal voltage should not drop below 9.5 volts at the end of 15 seconds while the current is flowing. When the battery is at 30°F (-1°C) the minimum battery voltage needed for this test is only 9.0 volts or above. If the test is performed on a battery with a hydrometer reading below 1225 the terminal voltage at the end of a capacity test will be very low but this voltage reading serves no useful purpose in determining the battery condition, because the test is only valid when performed on a battery whose state-of-charge is above 1225. A battery with a low state-of-charge should be recharged before a capacity test is performed.

A battery with a low state-of-charge is not able to supply the amount of electrical current required for cranking the engine and still have sufficient voltage remaining to produce an adequate ignition spark. Before any electrical system checking is done the battery should be checked to be sure that it is at least three-quarters charged (1225) and that it has satisfactory capacity. If the battery meets these requirements the technician can proceed with electrical system testing. If the battery does not meet the requirements it should either be charged or temporarily replaced with a good fully charged battery.

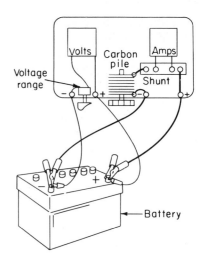

Fig. 2-4 Instrument hookup used to measure the battery capacity with a high discharge test.

2-3 CRANKING MOTOR CIRCUIT

Half of the main cranking motor electrical circuit consists of a heavy cable connecting the positive battery post to the starter terminal through a heavy-duty switch, relay, or solenoid. In the other half of the circuit, the negative battery post is connected to the engine block through a battery ground cable. This circuit carries high current while the engine is being cranked so it must have minimum resistance.

The rest of the vehicle electrical system is connected to the battery-starter insulated circuit at a junction between the battery and starter relay or solenoid. This junction might be the battery cable clamp, the battery junction of the solenoid, or a special junction block. The ignition switch is also fed from this junction. When the ignition switch is turned to the start position it energizes the relay or solenoid to operate the starter and crank the engine. This part of the electrical system is called the *starter switch circuit.*

2-4 CRANKING VOLTAGE

The starting system can be given an overall check by measuring the cranking voltage. To keep the engine from starting during this test, the coil secondary cable can be removed from the distributor cap center tower and placed against the engine block. An alternate method is to connect a jumper wire from the *distributor side* of the coil primary to ground. The negative voltmeter lead is connected to the engine metal for ground. The positive voltmeter lead is connected to the battery cable terminal of the starter. When the engine is cranked with

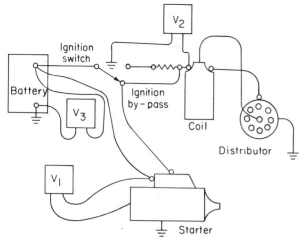

Fig. 2-5 Starter cranking voltage test connections.

or with the starter itself. Details of the test procedures used to pinpoint these problems are beyond the scope of this book.

2-5 CHARGING SYSTEM CIRCUITS

The alternator is the source of electrical energy used to operate all of the electrical devices on the automobile while the engine is running. In addition, the alternator has extra capacity to recharge the battery. The charging circuit consists of wiring that interconnects the alternator, the regulator, the battery, and the vehicle electrical system.

The main portion of the insulated circuit consists of a wire between the alternator BAT terminal and a junction where the alternator can feed both the vehicle electrical system and the battery. A second wire between this junction and the battery completes the insulated portion of the charging circuit. The battery uses this second wire to feed the vehicle electrical system when the alternator does not supply adequate electrical power by itself. Vehicle manufacturers use a number of different junction points. The junction may be the BAT terminal of the starter solenoid, a junction block on the radiator support or inner fender pan, or the BAT terminal of the horn relay. The grounded portion of the charging circuit is the metal to metal contact between the alternator case and the engine. The engine is connected to the negative battery post by the battery ground cable that completes the main charging circuit.

The voltage regulator is an important part of the charging system. It is connected in series with

the ignition key the cranking voltage should be above 9.5 volts when the starter is cranking at normal speeds. Cranking should be limited to the shortest cranking period necessary to get a stable voltage reading. An alternate location that is more accessible is to connect the positive voltmeter lead to the switch side of the coil. The minimum cranking voltage at the coil should be 9.0 volts. In some cases cranking voltage is measured across the battery posts while the engine is cranking. With this connection cranking voltage should be above 9.6 volts. Manufacturers' specifications should always be followed. In a normal warmed-up engine in good condition the cranking voltage will usually be 10.0 volts or slightly more. A technician should make a habit of placing the transmission in *neutral* and setting the *parking brake* when cranking the engine, especially when he uses a remote-control starter switch.

Cranking voltages lower than 9.0 volts indicate problems with battery cables and their connections

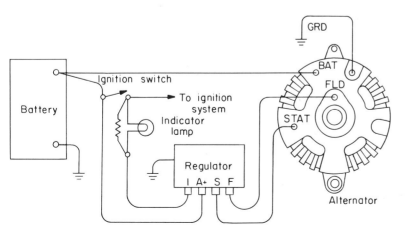

Fig. 2-6 Alternator charging circuit using an indicator lamp.

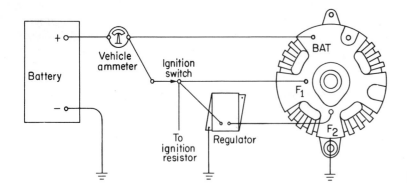

Fig. 2-7 Alternator charging circuit using an ammeter.

the alternator rotor field winding to control electrical current going through the field, thereby controlling alternator output voltage. When mechanical regulators are used, one end of the regulator-field circuit is connected to the insulated circuit through a switch and the other end is connected to ground. Solid-state regulators are usually located between the rotor field and ground.

The switch in the regulator-field circuit is necessary to open the circuit when the engine is not running and to close the circuit when the engine operates. The ignition switch serves this function. Some vehicles use a heavy-duty ignition switch to directly feed electrical power into the regulator-field circuit while others use a standard-duty ignition switch to signal a field relay located in the same case with the voltage regulator. The relay connects the regulator-field circuit to the charging circuit.

The charging circuit includes an indicator, either an ammeter or an indicator lamp, to show battery charge or discharge. The ammeter, as used in Chrysler charging systems, is connected in the charging circuit between the junction and the battery. It will show *charge* when the alternator is producing excess output while charging the battery. It shows *discharge* when the alternator cannot supply enough electrical current by itself so that some of the current is also coming from the battery to help supply the electrical demand of the vehicle.

A simplified method of determining proper charging system operation can be made with a voltmeter connected across the battery posts. Battery voltage is noted before starting the engine. After starting, the engine speed is increased and held at 1500 rpm. When all electrical systems are off the voltage should increase and hold at about 14.0 to 14.5 volts. When all of the electrical systems are turned on the voltage should drop to about 13.0 to 13.5 volts. If these voltages are not reached or if they are exceeded the charging system requires a thorough diagnosis to determine the problem. Details of these test procedures are beyond the scope of this book.

REVIEW QUESTIONS

1. What is the hydrometer reading of a fully charged battery?

2. What temperature correction factors are applied to the specific gravity measurement.

3. What test measures the ability of the battery to rapidly convert chemical energy to electrical energy?

4. What minimum hydrometer reading is required when making a battery capacity test?

5. What is the minimum battery terminal voltage of a healthy, fully charged battery after a load that is three times the battery ampere hour rating is applied to the battery for 15 seconds?

6. What is the minimum cranking voltage at the battery side of the ignition coil that can be expected on a warm normal engine? How does this change when measured at the battery posts?

7. How does the regulator control the generator output voltage?

8. What does the charge indicator show about the charging system?

9. What charging system voltage can be expected from a normal charging system with a fully charged battery when the ignition system is the only electrical system in operation?

3

Gasoline and Combustion

All of the energy required to operate an engine comes from the fuel. In a spark-ignited engine the fuel is gasoline. Gasoline is almost entirely composed of relatively volatile hydrocarbon molecules that have widely varying physical and chemical properties. It is designed and blended to meet the wide range of operating conditions found in spark ignited reciprocating engines.

The hydrocarbons in gasoline vaporize and start to decompose at temperatures below 600° F (320°C) which are encountered in the combustion chamber before ignition takes place. The products of combustion are mostly gases and a large quantity of heat energy. The heat increases the gas's pressure in the combustion chamber to produce the force on the piston that is required to operate the engine.

The liquid gasoline must be changed to a vapor to burn in an engine. In engines using a carburetor to mix the correct proportions of liquid fuel and air, vaporization of the gasoline must be done in one third of a second at idle speeds and in one thirtieth of a second at normal operating speeds. In fuel injected engines this must occur much faster. The carburetor aids the vaporization process by breaking the liquid gasoline into a sudsy foam that rapidly mixes with the air. The correct number of molecules of fuel must combine with the correct number of molecules of oxygen in the air. At sea level the air is dense so a relatively small quantity is required for a given amount of gasoline. The air becomes less dense at high altitudes and at high atmospheric temperatures so the same volume of air contains a smaller number of oxygen molecules. This causes the charge mixture to become richer. It becomes so critical on some emission controlled engines that leaner carburetor settings are required on automobiles used in the mountains than those used at sea level. Because automobiles are frequently operated in both mountains and at sea level some carburetors are being provided with altitude compensation devices to prevent over-rich mixtures at high elevations.

The combustion process takes place in the combustion cycle after the intake valve closes and before the exhaust valve opens. With the charge trapped in the combustion chamber the molecules of oxygen in the air come into intimate contact with the hydrocarbon molecules of the gasoline. This enables them to burn rapidly.

When a gallon of gasoline is completely burned it produces nearly a gallon of water, as well as sulfur dioxide in an amount equivalent to the sulfur content in the gasoline. At normal operating temperatures the water is in a vapor form so it leaves the cylinder as a part of the exhaust gas. Condensed water vapor is visible in the engine exhaust when the engine is first started in cold weather. Condensed moisture with sulfur dioxide makes the water acidic and corrosive. When the engine is cold much of the moisture is condensed inside the engine, especially during low temperature operating conditions such as suburban driving. The combination of corrosion and wear under these conditions is the major reason for excessive wear of the top ring area of the cylinder wall.

3-1 NORMAL COMBUSTION

A spark plug ignites the combustion chamber charge near the end of the compression stroke. The spark produced across the spark plug electrodes at the correct instant must have sufficient energy to raise the gas temperature between the electrodes to a point at which the charge burning becomes self-sustaining. From this point, a flame front moves smoothly across the combustion chamber during normal combustion. Charge burning will take place during approximately fifty degrees of crankshaft rotation putting maximum force on the crankshaft. Actual combustion is much more complex than it first appears from this simplified description. In

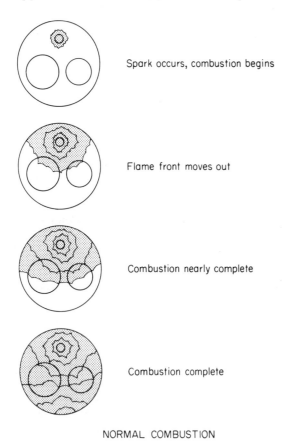

Spark occurs, combustion begins

Flame front moves out

Combustion nearly complete

Combustion complete

NORMAL COMBUSTION

Fig. 3-1 Flame front movement during normal combustion.

reality, the combustion gases go through many steps or phases during the combustion process. For this discussion the combustion is divided into two steps, *preflame reactions* and *combustion.*

A simple example is helpful in understanding preflame reactions. If one were to light a piece of paper with a match, the paper would first turn brown as a result of preflame chemical reactions, then it would ignite, producing a flame. The charge in the combustion chamber reacts in a similar way. As the gases are compressed and the temperature rises, preflame chemical reactions take place in the compressed charge that change the character of the charge. These preflame reactions prepare the charge for burning.

After ignition takes place, the flame front moves out in a modified spherical fashion that depends upon combustion chamber turbulence. The heat energy released behind the flame front increases combustion chamber pressure and temperature. Higher combustion chamber pressure and temperature increase the preflame reactions in a portion of the charge, called the *end gases*, that remain ahead of the flame front. Preflame reactions become more rapid at higher engine compression ratios. When preflame reactions increase too rapidly, abnormal combustion results.

3-2 ABNORMAL COMBUSTION

Abnormal combustion may be divided into two main types—*knock* and *surface ignition.* Each of these types results in loss of power and in excessive temperature. Continued operation under either type of abnormal condition will result in physical damage to the engine.

Detonation. Engine knock or detonation is the result of rapid preflame reactions within the highly-stressed end gases. The reactions become so rapid that spontaneous ignition of the end gases occurs. This results in very rapid combustion rates within the end gases that are accompanied by high-frequency pressure waves. These waves hit against the combustion chamber walls and cause a vibration noise that is called knock or detonation.

Reducing Knock. The tendency for an engine to knock with a given fuel can be reduced by any method that will lower either combustion pressure and temperature, or both; or by any method that will reduce the time the end gases are subjected to high pressures and temperatures. In

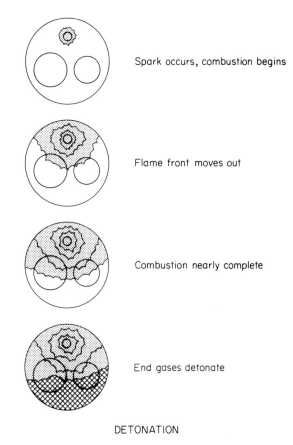

Spark occurs, combustion begins

Flame front moves out

Combustion nearly complete

End gases detonate

DETONATION

Fig. 3-2 Flame front movement during detonation.

addition, a change to a fuel that is less susceptible to rapid preflame reactions will reduce the tendency to knock. Octane rating is a measure of the antiknock properties of a fuel; a fuel that has high antiknock characteristics has a high octane rating.

Compression ratio has a major effect on compression pressure. As the compression pressure is increased, the power that an engine is able to develop increases. This is the result of the higher combustion pressures that are produced. High combustion pressures, however, cause a greater knock tendency. Fuels with high antiknock properties are used in higher-compression-ratio engines, thus allowing the engine to run knock-free while developing increased power. Lower compression

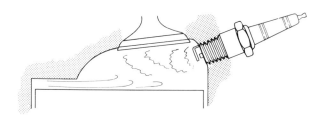

Fig. 3-3 End gases cooled in the quench area.

ratios are used in low-emission engines to enable them to run knock-free on low-octane unleaded gasoline.

Combustion chamber design also affects engine knock. Combustion chambers whose end gases are in a squash or quench area tend to have low knocking tendencies. This occurs because the end gases are thin and close to a cool metal surface. Cooling the gases causes a reduction and slowing of end gas preflame reactions, thus reducing the tendency of the engine to knock. This quenching of end gases is the main reason that a rotating combustion chamber engine will run knock-free on low-octane gasolines. Combustion chamber turbulence is also useful in reducing knocking tendency by mixing cool and hot gases, thereby preventing a concentration of static hot end gases in which rapid preflame reactions can take place.

Surface Ignition. Surface ignition is a broad term that indicates abnormal combustion starting at any source of ignition other than the spark plug. The effect of surface ignition, because it produces a secondary ignition source, is to complete the combustion process sooner than normal. The result is to have maximum pressure occur at the wrong time in the engine cycle; this causes the engine to develop less power.

One source of secondary ignition is a *hot spot*, such as a spark plug electrode, a protruding gasket, a sharp valve edge, etc. These items can become so hot during engine operation that they maintain enough heat energy to form a second source of ignition. These sources seldom occur in modern engine designs as long as the engines have proper maintenance.

Another source of secondary ignition is combustion chamber deposits. These deposits result from the type of fuel and oil used in the engine and from the type of operation to which the engine is subjected. Fuel and lubricant suppliers have been doing extensive research to produce products that minimize *deposit ignition*. A deposit ignition source may be a hot loose deposit flake that ignites one charge and is then exhausted from the engine with the spent exhaust gases. This is called a *wild ping*. Sometimes, the flake will remain attached to the combustion chamber wall. When this happens, it will ignite successive charges until the deposit is consumed or the engine operating conditions are changed.

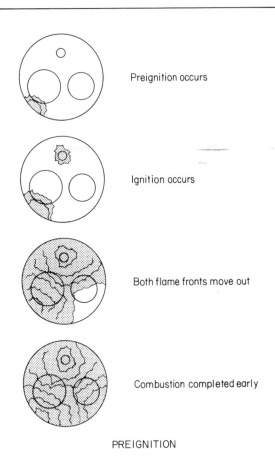

Preignition occurs

Ignition occurs

Both flame fronts move out

Combustion completed early

PREIGNITION

Fig. 3-4 Flame front movement during pre-ignition.

Names are given to many specific abnormal combustion conditions that are caused by surface ignition. If surface ignition occurs before the spark plug fires, it is called *pre-ignition*. It may be audible or inaudible. It may be a wild ping or it may be a continuous *runaway surface ignition*. If it occurs after the ignition is turned off, it is called *run-on* or *dieseling*.

Continuous pre-ignition can result in rapid engine damage, usually holes through the piston. Another phenomenon resulting from pre-ignition is engine *rumble*. Rumble is a low frequency vibration of the lower part of the engine that occurs when the maximum pressure is reached earlier than normal in the cycle. Rumble first became evident as a problem when engine manufacturers were able to greatly increase engine compression ratios as high-octane-rating fuels became available. This allowed the manufacturer to improve engine power with minor engine changes and with little thought

to increasing the strength of the engine crankshaft and block. Corrective measures were taken in succeeding engine models; therefore, rumble has been nearly eliminated from modern engines.

It is interesting to note that knock-resistant fuels and antiknock additives tend to increase combustion chamber deposits and, therefore, to increase the tendency to cause surface ignition. Fuel manufacturers have had to place additional additives in their gasoline to modify combustion chamber deposits in an attempt to reduce the deposit ignition tendency resulting from the antiknock additive deposits.

Abnormal combustion seldom occurs in modern mass-produced automotive engines when the recommended grade of fuel and motor oil is used and when the engine is maintained and adjusted correctly. Some problems may exist in engines that are used exclusively for low-speed, short-trip driving. Abnormal combustion frequently occurs in engines that are modified for maximum performance and in some cases in emission-controlled engines.

3-3 GASOLINE CHARACTERISTICS

Gasoline is made from petroleum. In its natural state petroleum is made up of many different kinds of hydrocarbon molecules. The smallest hydrocarbon molecules are in a gaseous form, such as natural gas and liquified petroleum gas (LPG). Next in size are gasoline molecules. Still larger molecules form diesel fuel, heating oil, and kerosene molecules. Very large molecules form the base for lubri-

Fig. 3-5 Piston damaged by abnormal combustion.

Fig. 3-6 Apparatus used to check gasoline volatility by distillation.

cating oil. The larger fuel molecules produce more heat energy as they are burned.

Because of the high economic value of gasoline some of the small gaseous molecules are combined in refineries to form more gasoline molecules, and some of the large molecules are split or cracked to make gasoline molecules. Modern techniques are capable of making more than one-half of each barrel of crude petroleum into gasoline.

Gasoline for automobile engines, called *motor gasoline*, must meet the needs of the engine. It must be clean and noncorrosive to the fuel-system parts. Motor gasoline must be light or sufficiently volatile to allow it to evaporate at low temperatures, so that the engine may be started, but not so volatile that it will evaporate in the fuel lines, causing vapor lock and thus preventing flow of liquid fuel. It also must not be so heavy that it will not evaporate or burn in the combustion chamber. If this happens, the unburned fuel will run down the cylinder wall, washing lubricating oil from the wall and diluting the motor oil. The volatility of the fuel is measured by a standard distillation test. In the test, a 100 milliliter (ml) sample is heated in a distillation flask. The vapors are led through a condenser and the condensate is collected in a

100 ml graduated cylinder. The temperatures of the vapors in the flask are recorded as each 10 ml is collected in the cylinder. The temperature-recovery curve is plotted on a distillation graph. The most volatile parts of the gasoline will evaporate at the lowest temperature, while the less volatile parts evaporate at higher temperatures. The distillation range of motor gasoline falls approximately between 90° F and 400° F (35°C and 205°C). The distillation curve is nearly the same for all motor gasolines sold in a geographic area regardless of the grade or brand.

Octane Number. The primary difference between gasoline grades is their antiknock quality. Premium brands of gasoline are made from selected refinery stock and most brands contain additional antiknock additives. They have a higher octane rating than regular gasoline grades. The octane rating is a scale that indicates the resistance of the gasoline to knock or detonation.

The fuel octane number is determined in a standardized, single-cylinder, variable-compression, fuel-research engine. The engine is first adjusted to standard conditions while operating on a reference fuel. Under these standard conditions, the knock meter (peak pressure measurement meter) is adjusted to mid-scale. The sample fuel to be tested is then run in the research engine under the same standard conditions as the reference fuel. Fuel mixture is adjusted to produce maximum knock, and the compression ratio is adjusted to produce the standard knock meter reading at mid-scale. While all conditions are kept constant, the engine is then run on reference fuel blends of known

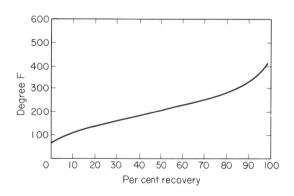

Fig. 3-7 Typical distillation graph for gasoline.

octane rating, one blend with slightly higher knock and one blend with slightly lower knock than the sample being tested. The sample fuel is assigned an octane number between the two reference blends. One primary reference fuel (PRF), isooctane, has been assigned 100 as an octane number and the other primary reference fuel, n-heptane, has been assigned 0 as an octane number. A blend of isooctane and n-heptane is used to test octane numbers below 100 octane; the octane number is given as the percentage of isooctane in the blend. For example, if the PRF blend contains 95% isooctane

and 5% n-heptane, the blend has a 95 octane rating. Octane numbers above 100 octane can be tested by adding specific amounts of tetraethyl lead to isooctane to make reference fuel blends above 100 octane. Different reference fuel blends necessary to "bracket" the sample fuel can be easily selected by referring to a table based on compression ratio that shows the approximate octane number.

Two different fuel research engines and test procedures are used to test motor gasoline. One procedure is called the *Research Method* and the other is called the *Motor Method*. The Research-Method engine is run at 600 rpm with the inlet air temperature adjusted to compensate for barometric pressures. The Motor-Method engine is run at 900 rpm and the air/fuel mixture temperature is held at 300°F. Gasoline will produce a different octane

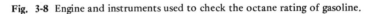

Fig. 3-8 Engine and instruments used to check the octane rating of gasoline.

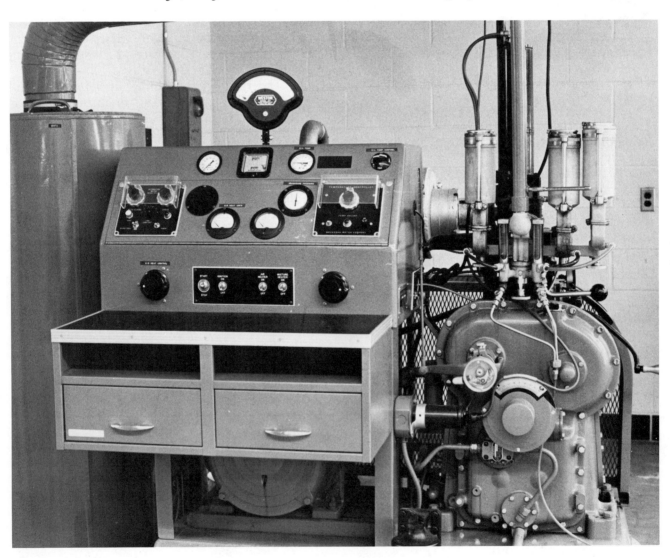

number by each test method. The Research Method usually gives a higher octane number than the Motor Method. The difference between these two octane numbers is called the fuel *sensitivity*. The sensitivity of the fuel is the result of the type of petroleum stock from which the gasoline was made. The octane number displayed on gasoline pumps is the average of the octane numbers determined by the Research and Motor Methods.

Octane Number Requirements. Gasoline has an octane number rating and each engine has a minimum octane requirement below which it will not run knock-free. The octane number requirement of the engine is the result of the engine combustion-chamber design; the operating mean effective pressure; the humidity of the charge; the temperature of the compressed charge; and the deposits present in the combustion chamber.

Two types of road tests are used to measure engine octane-number requirement. The Modified Uniontown procedure is a test to determine the minimum octane gasoline that is required under the most severe operating conditions of the fuel and engine combination. The Modified Borderline procedure tests the engine throughout its operating range and can be duplicated on a number of fuel samples. The Cooperative Research Council (CRC) selects a sample of automobiles each year to determine their octane requirements, and uses both test procedures to report engine octane requirements.

Details of these two tests are different; however, in both tests the engine is operated on the sample fuel at specified speeds, using specified ignition timing. The knock intensity is determined by ear and is reported as borderline, trace, moderate, or heavy knock.

In these road tests, the engine is operated on a primary reference fuel blend (isooctane and *n*-heptane) that is close to the octane number requirement expected. If the engine knocks more than required by the test procedure, the octane number of the reference fuel blend is raised and the test re-run. If it knocks less than required, the reference fuel blend is lowered. The octane number requirement of the engine is equivalent to the primary reference fuel blend that gives the specified knock intensity required by the test procedure.

3-4 GASOLINE SELECTION

The automobile operator must select the gasoline he will use from among the available service station grades of gasoline. His choice is made between premium, leaded regular, low-lead, or no-lead gasoline. He has a further choice between major brands and the so-called independent brands. His choice is limited by the lowest gasoline grade that will start and satisfactorily operate knock-free in his engine. Automobiles with catalytic converters have the fuel tank fill opening designed so leaded gasoline cannot be used.

The main difference in gasoline grades is the octane rating; premium has the highest octane rating and the highest cost while no-lead usually has the lowest octane rating and in some cases the lowest cost. Other gasoline characteristics, such as volatility, vapor pressure, specific gravity, and cleanliness are practically equal, regardless of the gasoline grade.

Octane rating is an index of the ability of the gasoline to resist knock during combustion at high pressures and temperatures. If an engine does not knock on a low octane gasoline it serves no useful purpose to use a higher octane gasoline. The higher octane gasoline will not produce more power or run cleaner than the low octane gasoline in an engine designed to operate on low octane gasoline. If the engine knocks, a higher octane gasoline is required by the engine. A tankful or two of low octane gasoline will not damage the engine if the operator reduces the throttle opening when knock is heard. By using different gasoline grades the operator can safely determine the lowest price gasoline that will satisfy his engine. One precaution should be observed. If the automobile owner's handbook does not specify the use of no-lead gasoline the owner should *not* use no-lead gasoline. Unless the engine valves and valve seats have been specially designed for the use of no-lead gasoline, valve seat failure may occur under high power operation using no-lead gasoline. An occasional tankful of no-lead gasoline will do no harm to the valves. If no-lead gasoline is specified, leaded gasoline should not be used because it will damage the catalytic converter.

There is some difference between the minimum octane gasoline specified in the automobile owner's handbook and the gasoline octane number as posted on the pumps at the gasoline station. The reason for this is that each uses a different rating method. Traditionally, the minimum octane number requirement of an engine has been based on the Research Method octane rating of the gasoline. The recent octane number marking on the gasoline pumps is really the Antiknock Index that has been approved by a joint committee of the Society of Automotive Engineers (SAE), The American Society for Testing Materials (ASTM), and the Coordinating Research Council (CRC). It more nearly relates the fuel antiknock characteristics to the engine's response. The rating is an average of the Research and Motor Methods and this gives a lower number than the Research Number for the same gasoline.

All grades of gasoline have their volatility changed or adjusted by the oil companies throughout the year for the expected seasonal changes in temperature and geographical variations in altitude. The customer has no choice among the five volatility classes (A, B, C, D, and E) that are provided for different months of the year and for different geographical locations. For example, the D volatility grade is a summer gasoline for Alaska, a spring and fall gasoline for Michigan, Missouri, and Oregon, and a winter gasoline for Alabama and Oklahoma.

For the lowest fuel cost the operator should select the lowest price gasoline of the type specified that will run knock-free in his automobile engine. He will purchase higher price gasoline if he wishes to have added personal services, if he desires to use a particular gasoline brand when he wants to buy gasoline on credit, or if it is inconvenient to get to a service station having a low priced gasoline.

REVIEW QUESTIONS

1. Why do air/fuel mixtures that are supplied by the carburetor become richer at higher geographic elevations and temperatures?

2. What makes the engine exhaust acidic and corrosive when the engine is operated at low temperatures?

3. How many degrees of crankshaft rotation are required for typical normal combustion?

4. What are two steps in the combustion process?

5. What is the name given to the unburned gases present in the combustion chamber during combustion?

6. What happens when preflame reactions occur too rapidly?

7. How does compression ratio effect engine knock?

8. What factors allow a rotating combustion chamber engine to run knock free on low octane gasoline?

9. What causes dieseling after the ignition is turned off?

10. What type of abnormal combustion is caused by combustion chamber deposits?

11. What must happen to gasoline before it can burn in the combustion chamber?

12. How does the volatility of regular leaded gasoline differ from unleaded gasoline in the same geographical area?

13. Name two primary reference fuels.

14. What limits the gasoline choice to be used in an engine?

15. What is the value of using a higher octane gasoline than the one specified for an engine?

4

Emission Control

Pollution has become a major problem throughout the world. This has led to a great deal of research in an attempt to stop additional pollution and to clean up presently polluted areas. Antipollution research indicates that the automobile is a major contributor to air pollution in the United States.

Air pollution is evident in a number of ways. It may be unsightly, as smoke, soot, or dust. It may be foul-smelling, as diesel odor or sewage treatment gases. The most serious type of air pollutants are those that present health hazards. Automobile emissions are considered to contribute to this last type of air pollution.

During the 1950's emission from automobiles was identified as a contributor to smog in the Los Angeles basin. The Los Angeles basin is a valley with the Pacific ocean on the west and mountains surrounding the other three sides. Prevailing west winds from the Pacific and the mountains tend to hold the air particles within the basin area. The usual shining California sun causes a photochemical reaction among the particles in the air that converts them to a yellow-brown haze called *smog*. It irritates the eyes, causes increased breathing problems, deteriorates some materials, and damages plant life.

Since the phenomena that produced smog were first identified in California, other cities have had large increases in the number of automobiles. When weather conditions are favorable the automobile emissions may be sufficient to form smog in any metropolitan area.

The principal products that are involved in photochemical smog formation are the hydrocarbons, usually the type called olefins and aromatics, and the oxides of nitrogen. Olefins are especially reactive in smog formation. They are straight-chain unsaturated hydrocarbon molecules with a double bond. The double bond is easily broken when other atoms are present to combine with the hydrocarbon molecule. In the presence of sunlight, these hydrocarbons and oxides of nitrogen are changed in a series of chemical reactions to produce smog components. The principal components of smog are: ozone, which is a powerful oxidizer that hardens rubber and is a health hazard in high concentrations; aldehydes, which are eye irritants; and a compound called peroxyacylnitrate (PAN), which terminates the photochemical reaction chain.

In a non-emission-controlled vehicle, crankcase vapors account for 25% of the total vehicle emission, the exhaust 60%. The remaining emissions evaporate from fuel tank and carburetor vents.

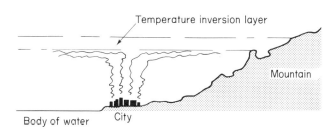

Fig. 4-1 Conditions conducive to smog formation.

4-1 HARMFUL EMISSIONS

Harmful exhaust emissions consist of carbon monoxide (CO), hydrocarbons (HC) and oxides of nitrogen (NO_X). Emission control devices on modern automotive engines are designed to keep them at a minimum.

The amount of carbon monoxide produced during combustion has been used for years as a measure of efficient combustion. A rich air/fuel mixture produces a large amount of carbon monoxide. As the mixture is leaned carbon monoxide is reduced until almost none is produced at an ideal cruising air/fuel mixture. Carbon monoxide does not contribute to the formation of smog but its emission is regulated by federal standards as a means of controlling efficient combustion and maintaining a healthy atmosphere. Carbon monoxide is harmful because it forms stable compounds in the blood stream that will block oxygen from acting with the hemoglobin in the blood. In low concentrations, it causes headache. In higher concentrations it leads to coma and death by asphyxiation.

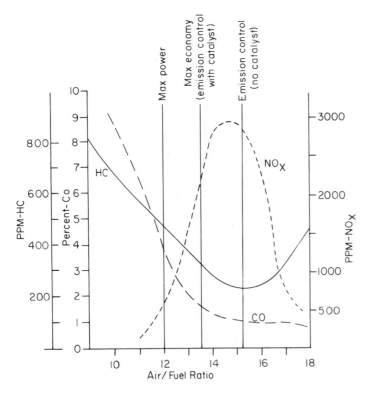

Fig. 4-2 Exhaust gas contaminant changes as the air/fuel ratio changes on a non-emission controlled engine.

Lowering the carbon monoxide level is accomplished by operating the engine as lean as possible while still preventing misfiring. Heating the lean mixture enables it to ignite more readily, thereby reducing the tendency to misfire at lean air/fuel mixtures. Most of the carbon monoxide forms during idling and during deceleration when rich mixtures are used to compensate for poor fuel distribution within the manifold. They also form when a cold engine is being choked.

One of the vehicle emissions that contributes to smog is unburned and partly burned hydrocarbons. Unburned hydrocarbons drift into the atmosphere as gasoline vapors while the gasoline tank is being filled. They leak out of the gasoline tank vents and from the carburetor float bowl vent when the engine is not operating. Some hydrocarbons also come from the combustion chamber when a cylinder misfires, when the carburetor mixture is too rich, or when the combustion chamber is cool.

Hydrocarbons, especially the olefins and aromatic types, contribute to the formation of photochemical smog. In the amounts in which they are normally present in the atmosphere, they have no direct harmful effect on a person's health. Unburned hydrocarbons in the exhaust are reduced by leaning the mixture, just as CO is reduced. If the mixture becomes so lean that the engine misfires, the unburned hydrocarbons *increase* greatly while CO remains low.

Most of the unburned hydrocarbons are produced by the surface quenching action of the combustion charge caused by the cooling effect of the metal surface of the combustion chamber. This is impossible to avoid. The quenching effect is reduced by redesigning the engine to reduce the combustion chamber surface-to-volume ratio. To do this the engine bore is reduced and the stroke increased. The rotary combustion chamber engine has a very high combustion chamber surface area compared to its volume and it therefore produces large amounts of unburned hydrocarbons.

The second smog-producing constituent produced in the combustion chamber is oxides of nitrogen (NO_X). They form when air, which consists of approximately 80% nitrogen and 20% oxygen, chemically reacts to combine these elements in a high temperature environment. The engine combustion chamber provides this high temperature environment. Engine thermal efficiency and power will increase as engine temperature increases. This also increases the production of oxides of nitrogen. The higher the peak cycle temperature, the greater the production of NO_X. The production of NO_X also increases as the mixture is leaned until an excessively lean mixture occurs. This, of course, causes misfiring, which results in an increase in unburned HC. Because the rotary combustion chamber engine operates at low thermal efficiencies it produces small amounts of NO_X. Diesels and turbines operate at high temperatures with large quantities of air and so they produce large amounts of NO_X.

Lead in the quantities that are present in gasoline produces no identifiable health hazard in itself. Lead is being eliminated from gasoline to minimize contamination of the catalyst in converters that are used on most 1975 and later model automobiles using spark-ignited internal combustion engines. These converters will help to oxidize the HC and CO, and to reduce NO_X to harmless products. It is easier to oxidize the HC and CO products than it is to reduce NO_X. This makes it easier to lower the amount of controlled emissions in the exhaust from a rotating combustion engine than it is to lower the amount of those emissions in the exhaust from piston engines.

4-2 EMISSION REDUCTION

California leads the nation in passing laws that require new automobiles to produce less emissions of the type that lead to the development of smog. Federal emission-control regulations for new automobiles are now in effect for the whole country. Automobile manufacturers have met the requirements of the first emission laws by providing the engine with positive crankcase ventilation. Additional laws followed and the automobile manufacturers have met their requirements. Carburetor

and intake systems have been modified to provide each combustion chamber with a mixture that more nearly meets ideal combustion requirements. The ignition system is designed to provide ignition at a time in the combustion cycle that results in lower smog-producing emissions. Combustion chamber designs and coolant temperatures have been changed to reduce harmful emissions. The exhaust system has been modified to aid in the combustion of products not fully burned within the combustion chamber. Vapors from the fuel tank and carburetor are vented to an activated carbon charcoal canister where they are trapped and stored to keep them from drifting into the atmosphere.

Vehicle emissions come from the engine crankcase, gasoline tank, carburetor, and exhaust. The crankcase vapors from engines built since 1968 are completely controlled. Evaporative vapors from the gasoline tank and carburetor are controlled under almost every condition in automobiles built since 1971. In order to run, the engine will use large amounts of air and expel a large quantity of exhaust, and so engine exhaust cannot be eliminated. Federal standards require the exhaust gases to be modified so that they contain only a very small percentage of harmful exhaust components.

This section describes the most common emission-control systems in use at the time this chapter was written. Variations of these systems are used for special applications. Later designs will, no doubt, be on the market by the time this book is published. It is therefore important to follow cur-

Fig. 4-3 Typical emission controls used on modern engines (GM Research Laboratories, General Motors Corporation).

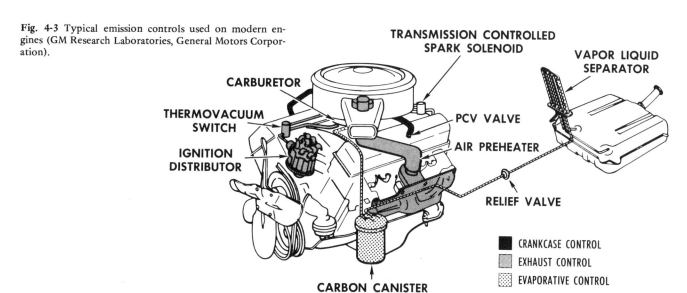

TRANSMISSION CONTROLLED
SPARK SOLENOID

VAPOR LIQUID
SEPARATOR

CARBURETOR

THERMOVACUUM
SWITCH

IGNITION
DISTRIBUTOR

PCV VALVE

AIR PREHEATER

RELIEF VALVE

CARBON CANISTER

■ CRANKCASE CONTROL
▨ EXHAUST CONTROL
▧ EVAPORATIVE CONTROL

rent specifications and procedure manuals when working on emission control vehicles.

Crankcase Emission Control. Crankcase vapors are a combination of light hydrocarbons, crankcase oil vapors, and combustion chamber gases that have been blown past the pistons and rings during the compression and power strokes. Crankcase oil vapors are the light volatile portions of the motor oil that evaporate at engine operating temperatures. Combustion chamber gases that find their way into the crankcase are blow-by gases, primarily made up of gases that come from the quench area within 0.002 in. to 0.020 in. (0.05 mm to 0.5 mm) of the combustion chamber wall surface. These gases are cooled by the relatively low-temperature combustion-chamber wall surface until they are too cool to burn. This explanation is supported by tests which show that blow-by gases have the same olefinic content as the gasoline being used, which indicates that these blow-by gases are unburned. Every time a driver opens the throttle, the blow-by rate increases, even though the throttle is not held open long enough to increase vehicle speed.

A hose between the air cleaner and rocker cover allows filtered air to enter the engine to ventilate the crankcase. The air circulates through the engine, picking up blow-by gases and oil vapors. Blow-by gases combine with oil vapors and fresh air to form crankcase vapors. Crankcase vapors are drawn from the crankcase through a *positive crankcase ventilation* (PCV) valve and a hose leading to engine manifold where vacuum will draw the gases to be burned in the combustion chamber.

The PCV valve controls the crankcase emission system operation. At high manifold vacuum a spring loaded plunger in the PCV valve is pulled against an opening to form a restriction in the valve. At idle and low speed when manifold vacuum is high, very little crankcase vapor is produced and so a low flow through the PCV valve is sufficient to keep the crankcase clean. High air flow through the PCV system at idle and at low speed would severely lean the air/fuel mixture delivered to the engine, causing poor drivability.

As the throttle is opened engine speeds increase, blow-by increases, and the manifold vacuum decreases. With this change in pressure the spring opens the PCV plunger to allow increased crankcase ventilation. With a large volume of air/fuel mixture flowing through the carburetor and manifold at high engine speeds, the increased volume of crankcase vapors allowed to enter the manifold

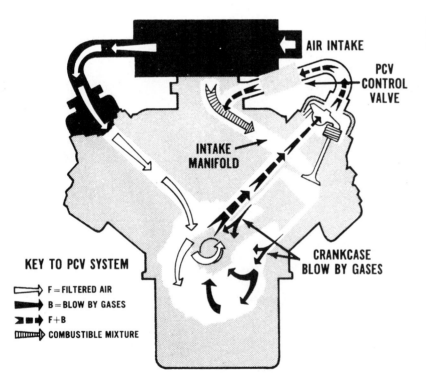

Fig. 4-4 Crankcase emissions are controlled by the positive crankcase ventilation system (GM Research Laboratories, General Motors Corporation).

AIR INTAKE

PCV CONTROL VALVE

INTAKE MANIFOLD

CRANKCASE BLOW BY GASES

KEY TO PCV SYSTEM

F = FILTERED AIR
B = BLOW BY GASES
F + B
COMBUSTIBLE MIXTURE

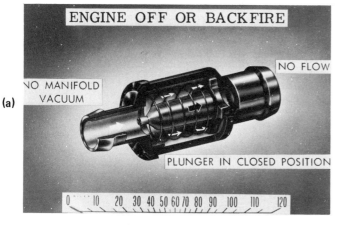

ENGINE OFF OR BACKFIRE

(a)

NO MANIFOLD VACUUM

NO FLOW

PLUNGER IN CLOSED POSITION

0 10 20 30 40 50 60 70 80 90 100 110 120

IDLING OR LOW SPEED

(b)

HIGH MANIFOLD VACUUM

MINIMUM FLOW

PLUNGER IN SEATED POSITION

0 10 20 30 40 50 60 70 80 90 100 110 120

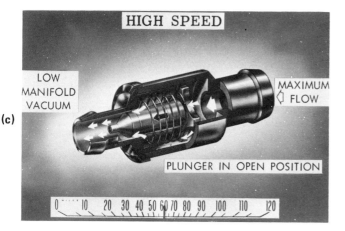

HIGH SPEED

(c)

LOW MANIFOLD VACUUM

MAXIMUM FLOW

PLUNGER IN OPEN POSITION

0 10 20 30 40 50 60 70 80 90 100 110 120

Fig. 4-5 Positive crankcase ventilation valve operation (AC Spark Plug Division, General Motors Corporation). (a) Valve position with plunger closed, (b) valve position with plunger seated, (c) valve position with plunger open.

through the PCV valve is insignificant. The PCV valve plunger balances between engine vacuum and spring pressure to provide proper ventilation at all normal speeds and all normal power settings. Full power at low speed may produce more blow-by than the PCV valve can handle. The vapors will then vent through the inlet hose and carburetor.

In operation the PCV valve and hoses may become filled with gummy deposits that restrict their action. It is recommended that they be replaced at regular intervals, such as 12 months or 12,000 miles (19,320 km), to keep the system operating properly. When the PCV system is operating properly it completely controls all emissions from the engine crankcase.

Evaporative Emission Control. The last vehicle emission to be controlled was evaporative loss from the fuel tank and from the carburetor vents. California started controls of evaporative losses in 1970. The controls were extended to apply to the entire United States in 1971. Evaporative losses are the result of the evaporation of highly volatile portions of the gasoline. They are entirely unburned hydrocarbons. These volatile portions of the gasoline provide vapors necessary for starting a cold engine. Their use in gasoline also allows the petroleum refiners to use a large portion of the crude petroleum stock to make gasoline and thus keep the gasoline price as low as possible. Petroleum producers and vehicle manufacturers work together to provide gasoline that will function satisfactorily in the engine at a reasonable cost to the consumer.

Gasoline evaporation is no longer allowed to vent into the atmosphere but the vapors are directed through tubing to a canister filled with

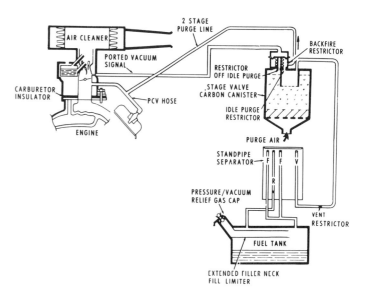

Fig. 4-6 Typical evaporative emission control system (AC Spark Plug Division, General Motors Corporation).

activated carbon or charcoal. Vapors given off by the gasoline in the tank and in the carburetor when the engine is not running are piped to the activated-carbon canister where they are absorbed. When the engine is restarted fresh air is drawn through the activated carbon. The incoming fresh air purges or removes the vapors from the activated carbon and carries them into the intake manifold to be burned in the combustion chamber.

Many carburetors used on evaporative systems have a vent that opens any time the throttle is fully closed to allow carburetor bowl vapors to flow through tubing to the canister. Some carburetors vent into the air cleaner and have no external vents. The gasoline tank vent system is more complicated. It has baffles that maintain an air space above the gasoline even when the tank is completely filled. Vents are led from each corner of the tank and from the air space above the gasoline to a *vapor separator*. This arrangement allows the vapors to leave the tank when the vehicle is parked in any position and at the same time retains the liquid gasoline in the tank. The vapor separator is usually a chamber positioned in a body panel, in a rear quarter panel, above the gasoline tank, or in the trunk directly behind the rear seat. Vapors go to the top of the separator while the accumulated gasoline liquid is returned to the tank. Vapors from the top of the separator are led through a tube to the carbon canister where they are absorbed. The tank is equipped with a pressure/vacuum fill cap that completely closes the filler opening. Pressure will build up in the tank from the gasoline vapor pressure that is normally produced as the gasoline evaporates. Vacuum may occur at times as the engine draws gasoline from the tank if air is not allowed to enter the tank to take the place of the gasoline withdrawn. All air or vapors entering or leaving the gasoline tank go through the activated carbon canister. The pressure/vacuum valve in the tank filler cap will open if either tank pressure or vacuum becomes excessive.

Exhaust Emission Control. Exhaust emission control is accomplished by carefully controlling the air/fuel mixture being sent to the combustion chamber, by controlling the combustion process, and by eliminating any harmful emission products still remaining in the exhaust gases.

Unburned hydrocarbons and carbon monoxide emissions are most critical at idle and during acceleration and deceleration when the engine runs with a rich mixture. Oxides of nitrogen are produced at cruising speeds when the engine runs with lean air/fuel mixtures and high thermal efficiencies that are accompanied by high peak combustion temperatures.

Emission control starts with the carburetor. Emission-control carburetors are very carefully calibrated and adjusted to operate as lean as possible while they still provide each cylinder with a combustible mixture. With mixtures on the lean side of their design range the engine may tend to idle

(a)

(b)

Fig. 4-7 Parts of the evaporative emission system. (a) Canisters, (b) sectioned separator.

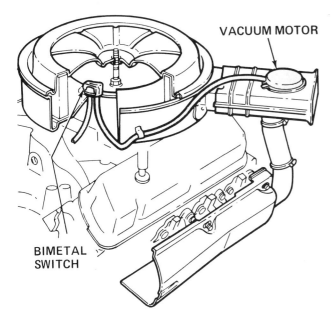

Fig. 4-8 Parts of an inlet air preheat mechanism (AC Spark Plug Division, General Motors Corporation).

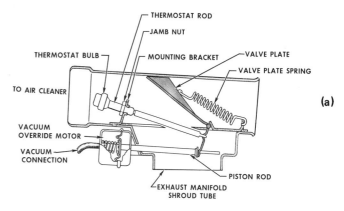

(a)

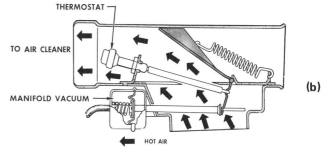

(b)

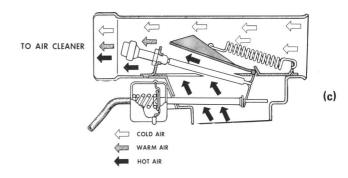

(c)

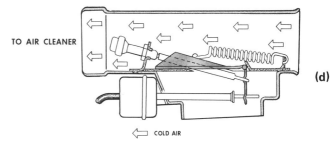

(d)

Fig. 4-9 Air preheater with thermostatic pellet control and vacuum override (AC Spark Plug Division, General Motors Corporation). (a) Part identification, (b) warm air supplied to a cold engine, (c) warm-cold air mix supplied to a partly warm engine, (d) cold air supplied to a warm engine.

rough and may surge during cruising operation. Careful carburetor adjustment will minimize this tendency.

When the engine is cold it must be partially choked to operate. This provides the engine with a rich air/fuel mixture that produces a large amount of unburned hydrocarbons and carbon monoxide. Emission-control engines have their chokes calibrated to open as rapidly as possible and still maintain drivability. This is done by heating the thermostatic choke-spring more rapidly or by using a more sensitive thermostatic choke-spring and vacuum break assembly. Some model engines use an electric heater to open the choke more rapidly than is possible using engine heat alone. Emission products that are produced by the engine will reduce as the choke opens.

Lean air/fuel mixtures ignite more readily if they are preheated. Emission control engines are provided with an intake air preheater. When the engine is cold, air is drawn through a shield placed around one exhaust manifold. As soon as the engine starts and the manifold becomes warm, manifold heat begins to warm this incoming air. The warmed air is ducted to an air cleaner inlet that is provided with a damper to allow only heated air to enter the engine. Heating continues until the temperature of the incoming air rises over 100°F (38°C). At this temperature the damper in the air cleaner begins to open to mix underhood or outside air with heated air coming from around the exhaust

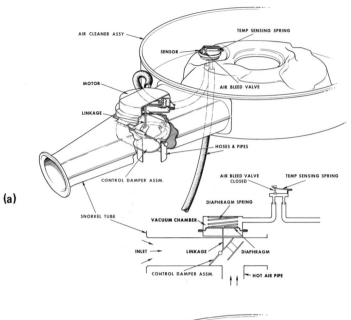

(a)

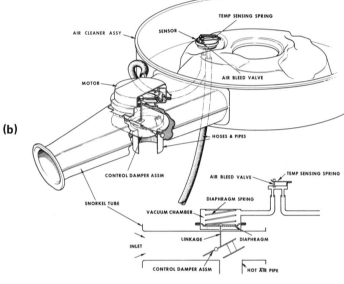

(b)

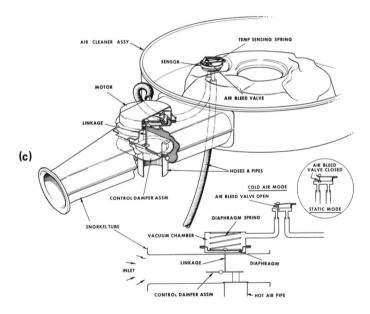

(c)

Fig. 4-10 Air preheater with a sensor controlled vacuum motor (AC Spark Plug Division, General Motors Corporation). (a) Supplying warm air to a cold engine, (b) supplying a warm-cold air mix to a partly warm engine, (c) supplying cold air to a warm engine.

manifold. Mixing continues until the incoming air reaches 135°F (57°C) at which time the damper has moved to the position that allows only under-hood or outside air to enter the air cleaner. The air damper may be controlled by a temperature-sensitive plastic pellet balanced against a spring force in a manner similar to a cooling system thermostat. It may also have a vacuum override that tends to increase the flow of heated air during acceleration. An alternate operating method is to use a temperature-sensitive spring to open a vacuum valve which in turn will control a vacuum diaphragm, sometimes called a vacuum motor, to properly position the air-control damper. The most usual cause of damper malfunctioning is cracked or incorrectly attached vacuum hoses.

Many factors affect combustion of the charge once it gets into the combustion chamber. The combustion chamber shape greatly affects the amount of unburned hydrocarbons remaining in the exhaust. The charge that is close to the combustion chamber surface is kept so cool that it does not burn, and these unburned gases form much of the unburned hydrocarbons in the exhaust. The areas of the combustion chamber that quench the

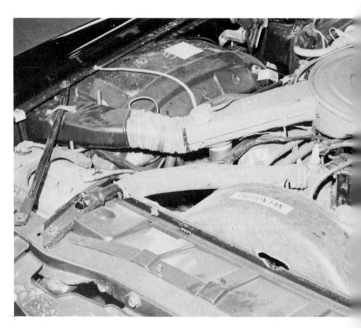

Fig. 4-11 Cold air supplied through a conduit from air outside the vehicle.

(a)

(b)

Fig. 4-12 Combustion chamber modified to reduce wall quenching. (a) High quench wedge head, (b) modified low quench head.

with a temperature-operated by-pass valve. At an engine temperature of approximately 220°F (104°C) the by-pass opens to provide distributor vacuum advance. This causes the engine to run more efficiently and this in turn increases the engine speed. Higher engine speed increases cooling-pump fan speed to cool the coolant faster and to pass more air across the engine; this results in a lower engine operating temperature.

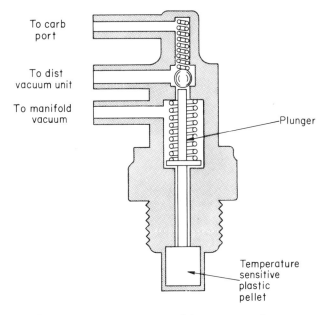

Fig. 4-13 Temperature operated by-pass valve showing internal parts.

charge have been kept to a minimum in emission-control engines.

To help burn lean mixtures, the combustion chamber temperature must be high. Increasing the operating temperatures of the cooling system thermostat helps to provide high combustion chamber temperatures. Temperatures are also kept high by restricting distributor vacuum advance that normally occurs on non-emission-controlled engines. High engine temperatures cause more rapid HC oxidation in the combustion chamber to lower the amount of HC remaining in the exhaust. While the engine is idling in traffic, coolant flow through the engine is low because the coolant pump is turned slowly and the fan is driven slowly. This condition may lead to excessive engine temperature. The distributor vacuum-advance system is provided

Engine emission-control systems using the features just described to clean up the exhaust are given a number of different names by the automobile manufacturers. They have essentially the same operating units and have names such as IMCO (Improved Combustion), CAP (Clean Air Package), CAS (Clean Air System), CCS (Controlled Combustion System), and Engine Modification.

Valve timing has a great effect on combustion. In a non-emission-controlled engine the valves were timed to give the engine efficient operation at its design speed. Low speed engines had a short valve opening duration and very little valve overlap. Overlap occurs when both valves are partly open between the exhaust and intake strokes. High speed engines have a long duration and a large valve overlap. Most emission-controlled engines have a

29

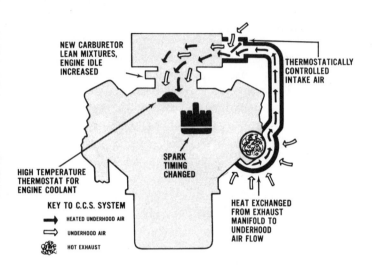

Fig. 4-14 Controlled combustion method of reducing exhaust emissions (GM Research Laboratories, General Motors Corporation).

short valve opening duration with a large valve overlap. The relatively short valve opening is normal for the low speed automobile engine. The large valve overlap allows some of the exhaust gas to return to the engine with the fresh intake charge. In some cases the exhaust manifold is restricted to increase back pressure. This dilutes the charge with the inert exhaust gas to minimize the amount of mixture used, thereby reducing the peak combustion charge temperature. Lowering the peak com-

bustion temperature results in a reduction of NO_x. Unfortunately, long valve overlap does contribute to a rough engine idle and poor low speed operation.

A second, more positive means of diluting the charge is with the addition of an exhaust gas recirculation (EGR) system. The system recirculates a portion of the exhaust gas back through the engine intake manifold. The exhaust gas takes up volume and will not burn. This leaves less space for the fresh charge to get into the combustion chamber. A smaller amount of combustible charge results in a lower peak combustion temperature and less NO_x production. The intake manifold exhaust crossover is a convenient place to interconnect the intake and exhaust systems. The EGR system in some engines consists of metered holes between the exhaust crossover and the intake manifold floor. Most EGR systems are equipped with a recirculating valve which limits exhaust gas recirculation so that it only occurs when the engine operating conditions tend to promote the formation of NO_x. These conditions are light acceleration and cruising speeds when the air/fuel mixture is lean. The exhaust gas recirculating valve is closed at idle and at low speeds; and gradually opens as the throttle is opened and manifold air velocity increases. It closes again at full throttle.

The EGR system may also be equipped with a valve that blocks EGR operation at low engine temperatures and low vehicle speeds. This is accomplished by a speed sensing unit in the speedometer cable and a temperature sensing unit in the engine cooling system. Some EGR valves are modulated by a backpressure transducer that senses

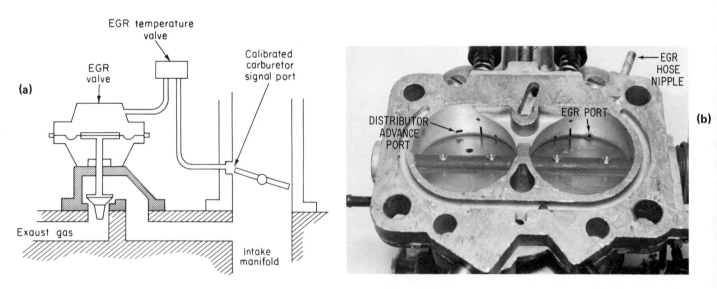

Fig. 4-15 Principles of exhaust gas recirculation. (a) System operation, (b) carburetor ports.

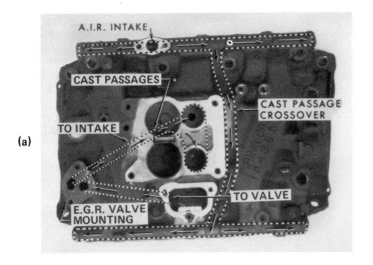

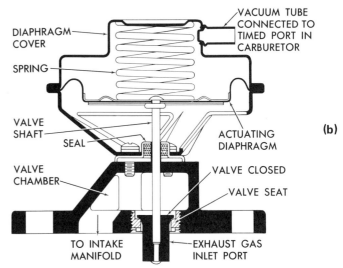

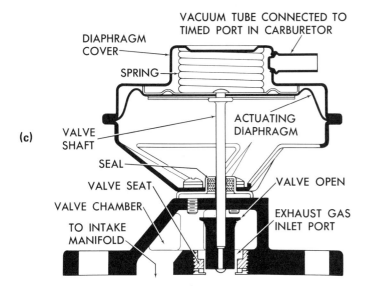

Fig. 4-16 Parts of the exhaust gas recirculation system. (a) A typical intake manifold with EGR porting (Buick Motor Division, General Motors Corporation), (b) (c) EGR valve closed and open (Cadillac Motor Car Division, General Motors Corporation), (d) back pressure modulated EGR.

pressure in the exhaust manifold. The EGR is turned off at full throttle.

After the exhaust gas leaves the combustion chamber it can be cleaned up using several different methods. The first method used was to pump fresh air into the exhaust manifold. The fresh air supplied additional oxygen that helped burn the HC and CO still remaining in the exhaust gases. This method does not affect engine efficiency, except for the small amount of power required to operate the air injection pump.

The vane type air injection pump, belt driven from the crankshaft, takes air in through a filter and pumps it through a diverter valve, check valve,

and injection tubes placed in the cylinder-head exhaust port or exhaust manifold. A *check valve* prevents back flow if exhaust pressure momentarily exceeds the air pump pressure. The *diverter valve* will by-pass pump-air to the atmosphere or to the intake manifold when the throttle is quickly closed. Quick throttle closure creates a high intake manifold vacuum that will draw a rich fuel mixture from the carburetor. This is too rich to ignite in the combustion chamber so it goes out the exhaust valve into the exhaust manifold. If fresh pump-air were forced into these rich exhaust gases the mixture would lean sufficiently to ignite when the next cylinder released hot exhaust gases into the exhaust

31

Fig. 4-17 Speed sensor to limit emission control operation.

Fig. 4-18 Temperature controls to limit emission control operation.

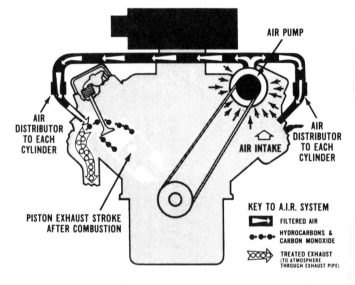

Fig. 4-19 System used to pump fresh air into the hot exhaust gases (GM Research Laboratories, General Motors Corporation).

system. This would result in an explosion in the exhaust system that could rip the muffler open. The diverter valve is therefore sometimes called a *backfire valve*.

The air pump emission-control systems have a number of different names depending on the manufacturer. They are called AG (Air Guard), AIR (Air Injection Reactor), Thermactor and Air Injection System. All operate in a similar manner and several use identical parts.

The air pump system is usually used with other exhaust emission-control devices to reduce exhaust emission products to acceptable levels.

Exhaust gas that cannot meet the federal standards using the above systems requires further modification. A thermal reactor can be installed in place of the exhaust manifold. It is an enclosed insulated series of chambers that maintains high exhaust gas temperatures for a longer period of time than is available during the power stroke. This gives time to more completely oxidize HC and CO products remaining in the exhaust gases. The thermal reactor takes a lot of under-hood space, runs hot, and has a relatively short life when compared to the simple exhaust manifold.

A more common device is a catalytic converter made of a bed of catalyst pellets or of a honeycomb grid of catalyst and installed in the exhaust system of late model automobiles. As the exhaust gas passes through the catalyst bed or grid,

the remaining objectionable exhaust contaminants are consumed at a much lower temperature than in the thermal reactor because of the action of the catalyst. An air injection system provides additional air that is required. The life of the catalyst will be shortened by contamination, especially lead contamination. Vehicles using a catalytic converter must be run on lead-free gasoline for the maximum life of the catalyst.

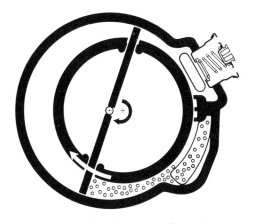

The vane is travelling from a small area into a larger area—consequently a vacuum is formed that draws fresh air into the pump.

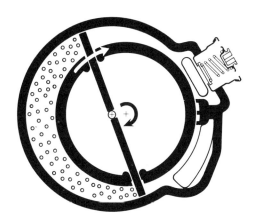

As the vane continues to rotate, the other vane has rotated past the inlet opening. Now the air that has just been drawn in is entrapped between the vanes. This entrapped air is then transferred into a smaller area and thus compressed.

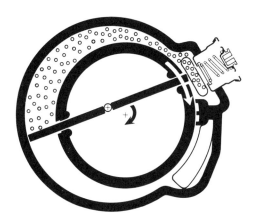

As the vane continues to rotate it passes the outlet cavity in the pump housing bore and exhausts the compressed air into the remainder of the system.

Fig. 4-20 Operation of the air pump (Chevrolet Motor Division, General Motors Corporation).

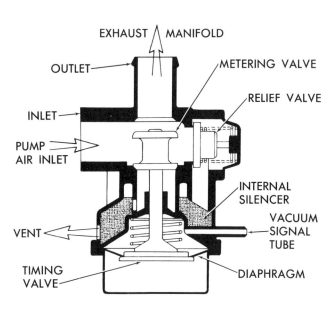

Fig. 4-21 Diverter valve operation (Cadillac Motor Car Division, General Motors Corporation).

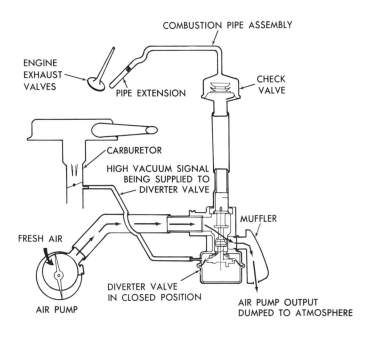

Fig. 4-22 Details of the air injection system (AC Spark Plug Division, General Motors Corporation).

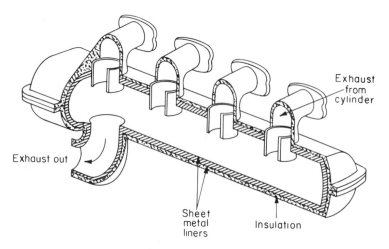

Exhaust
from
cylinder

Exhaust out

Sheet
metal
liners

Insulation

Fig. 4-23 Principles of a thermal reactor.

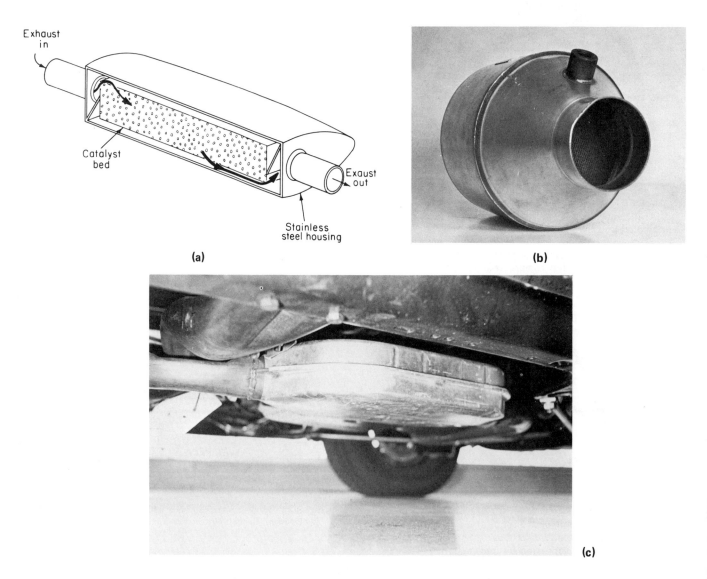

Exhaust
in

Catalyst
bed

Exaust
out

Stainless
steel housing

(a)

(b)

(c)

Fig. 4-24 Catalytic converter. (a) Pellet bed type, (b) honeycomb type, (c) typical installation.

A major problem in the control of vehicle emission is the measurement of these emissions. It is a time-consuming process that involves expensive equipment. Basic gas analysis is done using a chemical absorption process. In this process, a sample of a mixture of gases is run through a series of chemicals, one at a time. Each chemical absorbs one of the

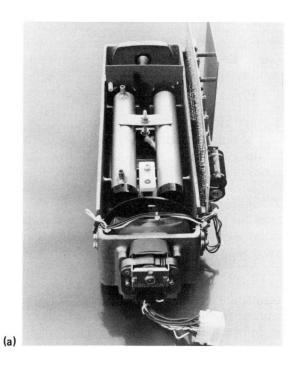

(a)

gases from the exhaust sample, which reduces the sample volume. The gas component removed is reported as a percentage of the entire sample.

Obtaining a good sample for chemical absorption is an associated problem. Exhaust samples may be trapped in a plastic bag and transferred to the laboratory for analysis. Evaporative vehicle emissions are taken from a sealed room or shed in which a vehicle has been placed. During a soak period, the vehicle and the room are kept at a specified temperature for a standard period of time prior to taking the evaporative emission sample.

A faster means of determining the exhaust emission is through the use of a nondispersive infrared analyzer (NDIR). This method has become an industry standard for measuring emissions. It is calibrated with specially prepared standard gas samples. The standard gas sample quality is checked by chemical absorption.

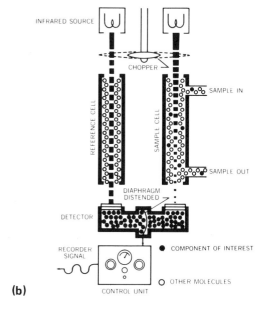

(b)

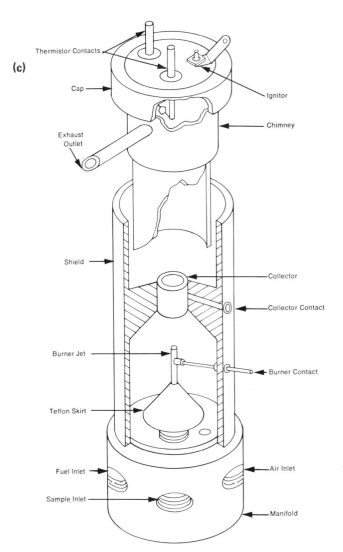

(c)

Fig. 4-25 Sensor used in an infrared tester. (a) Assembled unit, (b) principles (Beckman Instruments, Incorporated), (c) FID sensing unit (Beckman Instruments, Incorporated).

The infrared analyzer passes a pulsating infrared beam through each of two tubes or cells. The reference cell is filled with a nonabsorbing reference gas. The gas sample to be analyzed flows through the sample cell. Gases in the sample cell will absorb some of the energy of the infrared beam. After passing through the gases, each of the infrared beams hits a chamber adjacent to a balanced diaphragm detector. Both sides of the detector are filled with the gas type being examined. The amount of energy remaining in each beam increases the pressure in its side of the detector diaphragm. Unequal energy passing through the reference and sample gases will cause a difference in pressure in the detector chambers that deflects the diaphragm. Diaphragm deflection is proportional to the concentration of the gas sample being analyzed.

A separate analyzer is required for each gas component. Exhaust emissions are checked at the customer service level with nondispersive infrared analyzers for hydrocarbons (usually normal hexane) and carbon monoxide.

Hydrocarbon emissions are a combination of a number of different hydrocarbon gases. In early tests, automobile manufacturers measured only for hexane using a nondispersive infrared analyzer. This was inadequate for mass sampling. A flame ionization detector (FID) will indicate the amount of all unburned hydrocarbons in the exhaust sample quickly and accurately.

The heart of the FID tester is a hydrogen burner that produces a negligible number of ions. An ion is an atom with excess or missing electrons that makes the atom have an electrical charge. Introducing a sample of the exhaust gas containing unburned hydrocarbons produces a large number of ions proportional to the amount of hydrocarbon. A voltage difference between the burner jet and collector ring attracts the ions and thus produces a small current. The current is proportional to the number of ions produced. Electronic equipment amplifies the current flow signal and displays the results on a meter.

Exhaust emissions testing to meet federal standards requires the use of a $14,000 dynamometer and a minimum $25,000 instrument console in a room that has adequate ventilation and exhaust. These are usually backed up with a $75,000 computer. The California cycle sequence based on selected vehicle speeds under 30 mph is run seven times and requires approximately fifteen minutes. The mass cycle, consisting of a nonrepetitive series of idle, acceleration to 50 mph, cruise, and deceleration modes, takes nearly twenty-three minutes after a 12-hour soak period at room temperature. Exhaust emission analysis of this type is very expensive and is limited to vehicle development work and to quality control checks. It is not done as a part of tune-up procedure. A number of service-level instruments that measure hydrocarbons and carbon monoxide are available to help the technician do emission control maintenance.

No federal standards have been set for HC or CO emissions at the customer service level. Several states have passed laws and cities have passed ordinances regulating maximum allowable exhaust emissions as measured with automotive service-type test equipment. These laws are not uniform but they are quite liberal so that any automobile having reasonable maintenance will pass. The maximum limits of the test will pick out vehicles that produce an abnormal amount of polluting emissions.

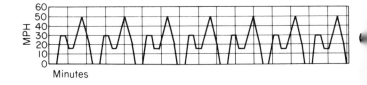

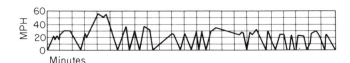

Fig. 4-26 Emission test cycles. (a) California cycle, (b) mass cycle.

REVIEW QUESTIONS

1. What method is used to lower the carbon monoxide level in the engine exhaust?

2. What engine operating conditions produce the most carbon monoxide?

3. What causes most of the unburned hydrocarbons in the exhaust?

4. What increases the production of oxides of nitrogen in the combustion chamber?

5. What makes up crankcase vapors?

6. Does the PCV system reduce the engine power or efficiency?

7. Does the evaporative control system reduce the engine power or efficiency?

8. During what operating conditions are oxides of nitrogen produced?

9. During what operating conditions are unburned hydrocarbons and carbon monoxide exhaust emissions most critical?

10. How does carburetor calibration help minimize emissions?

11. What device helps drivability of a cold engine?

12. How does temperature affect ignition of lean air/fuel mixtures?

13. What two means are used to dilute the inlet charge with an inert gas?

14. What was the first device used to clean the exhaust after it leaves the combustion chamber?

15. What is the purpose of the catalytic converter?

Carburetion Principles

5

The carburetor is only a part of the automobile fuel system. The rest of the fuel system consists of a fuel storage tank and a fuel transfer system combining a fuel pump, fuel filter, and connecting lines. The fuel system is required to keep an adequate fuel supply at the carburetor inlet at all times. An air filter is used to admit only clean air and an evaporative emission system is designed to keep gasoline vapors contained within the vehicle.

The carburetor is designed to mix air and fuel in proper proportions which will provide the correct air/fuel mixture for the engine operating conditions. It does this by sensing the operator's power demands and the engine needs through differences in pressure at various points within the carburetor. The sensing pressure at these points is called a pressure *signal*. Pressure signals are used to control the proper amount of fuel that is fed into the incoming air flow.

The air/fuel mixture leaves the carburetor as a mixture of air full of extremely small liquid fuel droplets, similar to liquid paint coming from a paint spray gun. These extremely small droplets are called *atomized fuel*. Most of the atomized fuel evaporates as it flows through the manifold from the carburetor to the combustion chamber to provide a combustible air/fuel mixture.

The carburetor is equipped with a number of specialized circuits to cover the wide range of air flow rates and air/fuel mixtures demanded by the driver and the engine. An idling engine uses a low air flow with a rich air/fuel mixture. At cruising conditions, the engine requires a moderate air flow and lean air/fuel mixture. During high speed operation the engine calls for a large flow of rich air/fuel mixture. The carburetor meets these needs and the additional requirement of providing short periods of rich air/fuel mixtures for starting and acceleration.

5-1 CARBURETION REQUIREMENTS

Engine fuel needs are first determined in an engine test laboratory at idle, cruise, and full power; then a carburetor is designed to meet them. The carburetor must supply the correct quality air/fuel mixture to the engine in a quantity that will meet the operator's demands between idle speeds and full throttle. It must match the engine needs to the operator's demands so that the engine will develop the power that the operator requires. It must do this as economically as possible. These basic engine fuel requirements are modified to help the engine meet emission regulations.

Fuel Ratio Requirements. In most spark ignited engines, the air and fuel are mixed and delivered to the combustion chamber as a combustible mixture. Combustible air/fuel mixtures range from an 8:1 to a 20:1 gasoline/air ratio by weight. The ideal mixture for the average gasoline is 14.8:1 in which the oxygen contained in the air is the correct amount required to burn the entire quantity of fuel. This is a *stoichiometric* mixture; that is, the substances are in the exact proportions required to complete the reaction. Internal combustion engines operate best on air/fuel ratios between 11.5:1 (rich) and 15:1 (lean), except at idle where engine mixtures may go as rich as 9.5:1 for cars built before 1968. For emission-controlled engines idle mixtures are approximately 14:1, with cruising mixtures as lean as 16:1 when operated near sea level.

Engine power results from expansion of the burned intake charge in the combustion chamber. In order to insure maximum expansion, which in turn will produce maximum power, it is necessary to have enough fuel to use all of the oxygen from the air. Air/fuel ratios of approximately 12:1 provide this rich mixture at high power settings.

To get maximum economy from an engine, all of the fuel must be burned so that the maximum amount of energy is released. In this case, an air/fuel ratio of 14.8:1 or leaner is used.

Fuel distribution in the intake manifold at idle speed is poor because low gas velocities through the manifold will allow the fuel to drop out of the mixture. A rich mixture is delivered by the carburetor so the leanest cylinders will still receive a

combustible mixture. Other cylinders, of course, receive an excessively rich mixture under idle conditions. Uneven mixture between cylinders will cause rough engine idle. Engines that are designed for minimum exhaust emissions run on leaner air/fuel ratios and higher engine idle speeds than is possible in engines without emission controls. Emission-controlled-engine manifolds are more carefully designed so that mixture distribution between cylinders is nearly equal.

It makes no difference if an engine is carbureted or fuel-injected, the engine still needs the same fuel mixture ratios. Fuel-injected engines that discharge fuel close to the intake valve have more even fuel mixture distribution to the cylinders than have carbureted engines because fuel injection does not depend upon air velocity and air/fuel mixing within the intake manifold to deliver the fuel to the cylinder. For this reason fuel injection is given consideration as a means of meeting strict emission regulation.

The carburetor or fuel injector supplies a rich mixture for idle, a lean mixture for cruising conditions, and a rich mixture for power and high speed operation. The air/fuel ratio compared to the air flow into the engine operating at cruising speeds would be plotted as Curve A in Figure 5-1. A full throttle air/fuel ratio would appear as Curve B.

The actual carburetor or fuel-injection system is built to a tolerance so that mixture ratios will fall near the ideal, within a flow band, as shown by the dotted lines. Emission carburetors are held to a very close tolerance. Emission driving cycles require a lean mixture at low speeds, and so the air/fuel ratio has a two-step staging for best drivability as shown in Curve D in Figure 5-1. After assembly, production carburetors are checked on a flow bench that will measure air and fuel flow at a number of vacuum settings. These are checked against a master graph that looks similar to Figure 5-1.

If a carburetor were to run *rich* beyond the tolerance, power would fall off and the engine would use excessive fuel. The unburned fuel may foul spark plugs and, in extreme cases, dilute the oil on the cylinder walls which, in turn, will cause excessive cylinder and piston-ring wear. It will also produce excessive hydrocarbon and carbon monoxide exhaust emissions and will produce poor gas mileage. If the carburetor were to run *lean* beyond the tolerance, power would also fall off. Excess-

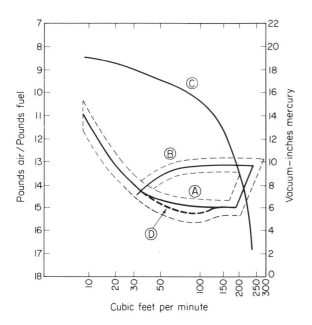

Fig. 5-1 Typical air/fuel ratio graph. Line A is cruising, Line B is full throttle, Line C is engine vacuum, and Line D is cruising on emission controlled engines.

ively lean mixtures cause misfiring, along with high localized temperatures that often cause pre-ignition and detonation. Eventually, these excessively lean mixtures produce burned spark plugs and valves. Lean misfiring does not burn the charge so unburned hydrocarbons appear in the exhaust and the engine produces poor gas mileage but the carbon monoxide emission remains normal.

Additional Considerations. The foregoing discussion assumes that the engine is operating at a constant speed under a constant load. This is called a *steady state*. Additional carburetor devices are required to give correct mixtures which will provide drivability. While the engine is cranking, air flow through the carburetor is very slow and the fuel is not broken into the desirable small droplets. Therefore, it will evaporate slowly. A *choke* is installed to provide a very rich mixture so that enough of the volatile portion of the gasoline will evaporate to produce a combustible mixture needed for starting.

The carburetor or fuel-injection system is required to supply small droplets of finely divided sudsy fuel to the incoming air in the correct proportion to meet the engine requirements. The sudsy liquid fuel evaporates rapidly from the surface of the very small atomized droplets. Smaller or finer droplets increase the evaporation rate. For maximum *volumetric* efficiency, about sixty percent of the fuel should be evaporated between the fuel discharge nozzle and the cylinder. The rest evaporates in the combustion chamber during compression. If a larger percentage of the gasoline evaporates there will be less room for air so the quantity of the charge is reduced. This in turn reduces maximum power.

When the engine is cold, manifold evaporation is slow and the engine oil is thick; therefore, more energy is required to keep the engine running. To keep the engine running until it becomes warm, the throttle is held slightly open with a carburetor device called a *fast idle cam*. This fast idle cam is usually controlled by a linkage from the choke, so that the cam will be released as the choke opens. Some emission carburetors are also supplied with an idle enrichment system to add fuel to a cold engine.

The throttle is opened suddenly to produce rapid acceleration. Air, with its low mass per unit volume, will start to flow much more quickly than the heavier fuel, momentarily causing the mixture to be lean. Carburetors are equipped with a device called an *acceleration pump* which provides extra fuel for a few seconds after the throttle is opened, until fuel can start to flow in the normal carburetor systems.

Fuel-injection systems are standard on a few passenger car engines. The details of their current production systems have not been made public and are therefore beyond the scope of this discussion. It should be remembered, however, that fuel-injection systems still must provide an air/fuel mixture ratio that the engine needs, just as a carburetor is required to do.

Carburetor Pressures. The air/fuel mixture delivered by a carburetor is controlled by differential pressures and different sized or metered openings for fuel and for air. To operate a carburetor correctly, it is necessary to establish base-line fuel and air pressures. The base-line fuel pressure is established by the fuel level in the carburetor float bowl or by fuel pressure in a fuel-injection system. The base-line air pressure is atmospheric pressure. As the pistons go down on their intake stroke, manifold pressure is lowered or depressed. To say it another way, vacuum is increased. Any increase in engine speed without a change in throttle position will increase the engine manifold vacuum. It should be noted that under these conditions, the engine manifold vacuum is an indication of the efficiency of the engine. With a fixed throttle and load, any change in ignition timing or fuel mixture that results in an increase in engine speed indicates more efficient combustion. Conversely, any decrease in vacuum indicates a decrease in engine efficiency. This difference in pressure between atmospheric pressure and manifold vacuum is the driving force that causes the air/fuel mixture to flow into the carburetor.

Air velocity through the large carburetor opening called a *barrel* is the result of atmospheric pressure forcing air into the partial vacuum that is within the manifold. As manifold vacuum increases when the throttle is closed, less air will flow into the engine. The greater the difference between atmospheric pressure and manifold vacuum, the greater the air velocity past the throttle plate and the greater the pressure forces that will occur within the carburetor.

Differential pressures create the *signals* within a carburetor that are used to control fuel flow into the air stream which, in turn, will create the air/fuel mixture needed. The quantity of fuel that flows through the sized carburetor fuel openings, called *jets*, is the direct result of jet size, jet shape, and difference in pressure between the upstream and downstream side of the jet.

A throttle plate is placed in the base of the barrel between the carburetor and the manifold so that the passage may be effectively closed. With the throttle nearly closed, atmospheric pressure cannot fill the manifold as rapidly as the pistons evacuate it, and so the engine has a high manifold vacuum that may also be called a *pressure depression*. As the throttle is opened, air enters the manifold, increasing the quantity of air flowing into the engine and decreasing manifold vacuum. At wide open throttle, manifold vacuum is very slight and air volume flowing through the carburetor is very high. Air, moving at high flow rates, causes pressure reduction within the air flow.

Fuel Pump. Fuel is delivered from the fuel tank to the carburetor by a fuel pump. The inlet stroke of the fuel-pump diaphragm is operated by a cam through a spring-loaded linkage. Fuel comes in from the tank through a one-way inlet check valve. It is forced out toward the carburetor

through an outlet check valve by a spring-loaded diaphragm. The amount of fuel pressure impressed on the carburetor is controlled by calibration of the fuel-pump spring.

5-2 CARBURETOR SYSTEMS

The following discussion will describe carburetor operation, with the main system described first and modifying units added as a need for them is shown. The carburetor system designs presented are those of mass-produced automotive carburetors.

Simple Carburetor—Main System. Air flowing through the carburetor must pass a restriction in the barrel called a *venturi* which increases inlet air velocity at the narrow portion or throat. This high velocity is accompanied by a lower pressure within the air stream. The change in pressure which results from the high velocity air flow, called *venturi vacuum*, is used as one of the signals to help meter the fuel flow.

The amount of fuel allowed to enter the carburetor is controlled by a float inlet valve and seat. It maintains a constant fuel level in the carburetor float bowl by opening or closing the inlet valve.

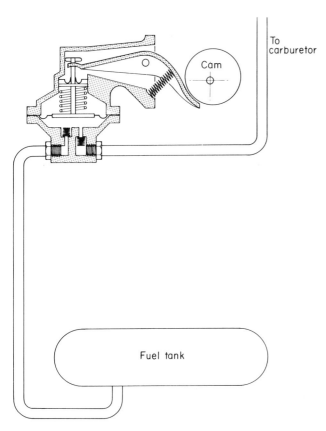

Fig. 5-2 Typical fuel pumping system.

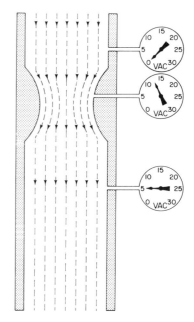

Fig. 5-3 Changes in pressure as air flows through the venturi.

This specified fuel level establishes the base-line fuel height or pressure head that is used for fuel flow control. Differential pressure that results from engine vacuum and high velocity air flow through the barrel air horn and venturi provides the signal required to force the correct quantity of fuel through metering devices within the carburetor.

The simplest carburetor consists of a float and valve system, a float bowl to hold the gasoline, an air horn with a venturi, a throttle plate to control the air flow through the carburetor, a fuel passage between the float bowl (fuel reservoir) and the venturi, and a metering jet for controlling fuel flow. In this simple carburetor, the discharge nozzle and venturi must be located *above* the fuel level, so that the fuel will not drop out of the nozzle when the engine is not running.

In simple carburetor operation, air flows into the manifold as the throttle plate is opened. The air flow reduces pressure within the venturi, producing a partial venturi vacuum. Atmospheric pressure, acting on the fuel through a vent in the float bowl forces some of the fuel through the metering jet into the *main well* and out of the discharge nozzle that is located within the narrowest portion of the venturi. This fuel mixes with the air as it is carried into the manifold.

The main metering jet is sized so that the air/fuel ratio delivered to the manifold is within a combustible range. As the throttle plate is opened still further, more air flows through the venturi, increasing venturi vacuum. This causes more fuel to

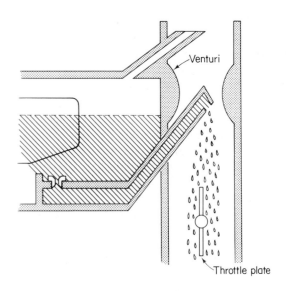

Fig. 5-5 Fuel flow from the carburetor nozzle.

flow, thus maintaining a combustible air/fuel mixture ratio.

This simple carburetor would have limited use, because it has a narrow range of operation. The air/fuel ratios do not remain constant, as has been suggested, because fuel, like other liquids, has *mass, surface tension*, and *adhesion*. Surface tension causes the fuel to hold together in large droplets, rather than breaking up into fine droplets that are necessary for rapid evaporation. Adhesion, which is the tendency of a liquid to cling to a surface, causes the fuel to break away from the discharging nozzle in large droplets. The viscosity of the fuel tends to restrict its flow.

In a simple carburetor, the pressure drop or vacuum increases faster in the venturi than the increase in air volume that flows through the venturi, so that the mixture of air and fuel gradually becomes richer as air flow increases. All automotive carburetors have some type of *compensating device* to correct for this enriching tendency. The most common of these devices is an *air bleed*.

An air bleed is a metered hole in the air horn above a passage leading to the main well. When a venturi vacuum exists at the discharge nozzle, air enters the main well through the air bleed. Here, air and fuel mix as they go from the main well to the discharge nozzle. This mixture of air and fuel causes the fuel to be broken into a sudsy air/fuel emulsion which reduces adhesion of the fuel to the passage walls. This occurs because the surface tension and viscosity of the sudsy mixture are less than those of the fuel alone. Air coming into the air bleed will also reduce the enriching effect of a plain discharge nozzle as shown as line B in Figure 5-6. The

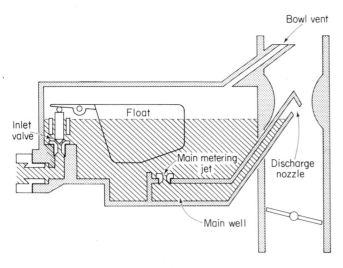

Fig. 5-4 A simple carburetor.

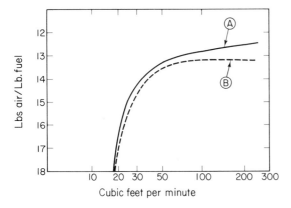

Fig. 5-6 Simple carburetor air/fuel curve A modified by a compensating air bleed to curve B.

into the main well as fuel flow discharge rate increases. This compensates for the normal enrichment characteristic of the plain discharge nozzle; it also helps to atomize the fuel being discharged into the air stream.

Air bleeds are sometimes designed to act as an *anti-percolator*. When a hot engine is turned off, the engine heat will warm the carburetor. This causes the volatile portion of the fuel to boil, vaporizing that part of the gasoline within the carburetor. The vapors are vented through the

effect of surface tension and adhesion is reduced when using an air bleed and so the air/fuel ratio will remain constant when correct size air bleeds are selected.

Many carburetors have a *perforated tube* in the main well or have a perforated air-well adjacent to the main well. To aid in the control of fuel flow, air may bleed through the perforated tube either from the outside inward or from the inside outward, depending on the particular carburetor design. The amount of fuel that flows into the main well is determined by the main jet size and design, and by the fuel level in the well. When the discharge nozzle rapidly draws fuel, the fuel level in the main well is lowered because the main jet cannot supply fuel fast enough. Holes in the main well tube compensator are gradually uncovered as fuel is drawn from the main well. This will let more air

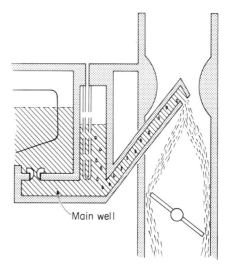

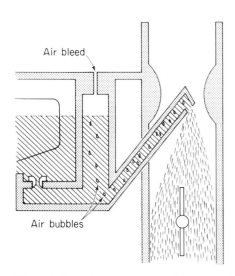

Fig. 5-7 Fuel flow from a nozzle with an air bleed compensator.

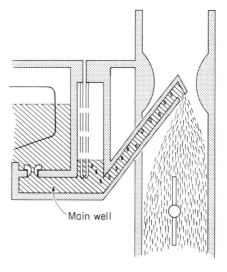

Fig. 5-8 Fuel level change in the main well as air flow increases through the venturi.

anti-percolator so that they will not build up pressure that forces raw fuel out of the discharge nozzle, flooding the manifold, a process called percolation. A properly placed air bleed will allow these vapors to be vented into the air horn, thus minimizing flooding and hot-start problems. Bowl vents, mechanically opened when the throttle is fully closed, will allow bowl vapors to vent from the carburetor rather than to push fuel out of the discharge nozzle. This helps to reduce hot-start problems, but it does add to overall vehicle emissions. Evaporative-emission-control carburetors have the float bowl vented to a vapor absorption system which will trap these unburned hydrocarbon evaporative emissions.

Another method of air/fuel mixture control is used by the constant-vacuum-type carburetor. This carburetor has a floating piston that nearly closes the carburetor barrel opening to form a venturi on the atmospheric side of the throttle plate. As the throttle is opened air flows through the small gap under the floating piston. A hole through the piston senses the increase in venturi vacuum as the air flow rate past the piston increases. The vacuum passage hole through the piston connects to a vacuum chamber above the piston. As venturi vacuum begins to increase, the piston is pulled up against a calibrated spring to enlarge the venturi opening and thereby effectively maintain constant vacuum.

(a)

(b)

Fig. 5-9 Typical mechanically opened float bowl vents. (a) External vented, (b) vent to a carbon canister.

(a)
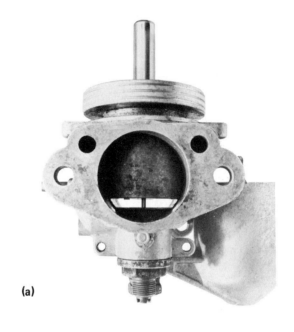

(b)

Fig. 5-10 Constant-vacuum carburetor with a floating piston. (a) Low speed position, (b) high speed position.

A long tapered fuel needle is attached to the bottom of the piston. When the carburetor is assembled the needle is centered in the main fuel jet. As the piston moves up it pulls the fuel needle with it so a smaller diameter section of the needle remains in the main fuel jet. This allows more fuel to flow around the needle as the piston rises to let more air flow into the engine. When the carburetor has a carefully sized and positioned needle, the air/fuel ratio delivered by the carburetor is closely controlled throughout the entire engine operating range.

Some of the constant-vacuum carburetors have a close-fitting piston to seal the vacuum chamber while others use a diaphragm as shown in the accompanying illustration. The principle of operation is the same.

Idle System. The carburetor main system previously described will allow an engine to run

(a)

GUIDE SLOT

VACUUM PASSAGE HOLE

FUEL METERING NEEDLE

(b)

Fig. 5-11 Constant-vacuum carburetor piston. (a) Out of the carburetor, (b) installed in a partially assembled carburetor, (c) diaphragm operated type on the left and piston operated type on the right.

(c)

45

with correct mixtures at cruising speeds. When the engine is slowed, air velocity through the venturi will decrease. At some point fuel delivery will decrease very rapidly, the mixture will be too lean to be combustible, and the engine will stop. To maintain engine operation at low speeds, an idle and low-speed system must be included in the carburetor.

Fuel for the idle system is usually taken from the main well up a passage to a point above the fuel level. The passage is often an *idle tube* that extends into the main well passage. In some carbure-

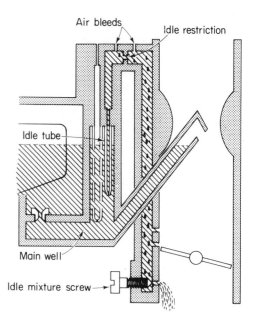

Fig. 5-14 Typical idle system.

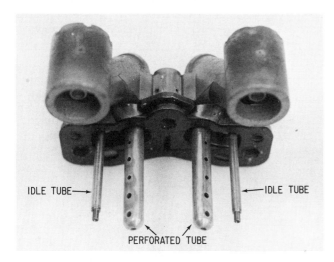

Fig. 5-12 Typical discharge cluster showing the location of the idle tube and perforated tubes that fit into the main well.

Fig. 5-13 Typical location of idle air bleeds.

tors, this idle tube has a metered orifice at its lower end. Usually, an idle air bleed is provided at the upper point.

The *idle air bleed* serves two functions. The first is similar to the main air bleed because it adds air to the fuel to reduce its viscosity and to help atomize it. Its second function is that of a "siphon breaker." With the idle discharge nozzle in its normal location below the fuel level, fuel would continue to flow when it was not needed if a siphon breaker were not used. The air bleed at the highest point in the idle system serves this siphon breaking function. In some modern carburetors, the idle air bleed will also help as an anti-percolator device when the engine is stopped, by providing a means to allow vapors to vent into the air horn.

From the idle air bleed, fuel is led down a passage past an idle restriction, sometimes called an economizer, to a port or opening just below the throttle plate, where high manifold vacuum exists as the engine is idling. Atmospheric pressure in the carburetor bowl pushes idle fuel through the main jet into the main well, up the idle tube where it picks up additional air at the air bleed, then down the passage through the idle restriction and out into the manifold vacuum below the throttle plate.

The engine requires a correct air/fuel mixture in sufficient volume to operate at its normal idle speed. The required air volume is supplied by the size of the air passage opening around the throttle plate. The fuel quantity is controlled by a manually-adjusted tapered idle needle fuel screw. This screw is usually located in an opening or idle port below

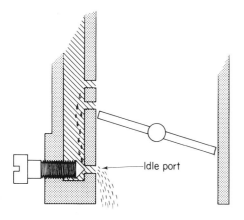

Fig. 5-15 Air and fuel flow at curb idle.

the throttle plate. As the needle is screwed into the port, fuel is restricted and the mixture becomes leaner. As the needle is backed out of the port, the effective port size is enlarged and the mixture is enriched. The fuel control screw adjusts engine idle smoothness. In some carburetors idle mixture is controlled by a tapered metering screw in the idle air bleed. Turning the screw in restricts the air bleed to enrich the idle mixture. The screw in the air bleed uses left hand threads and so turning the screw counterclockwise enriches the idle mixture and turning it clockwise leans the idle mixture, just as it does with the needle screw that controls the fuel quantity directly. In some emission-control carburetors a coolant temperature-controlled idle enrichment system controls the amount of idle air bleed.

As the throttle is opened from idle, vacuum acting on the idle port is reduced so that less fuel is supplied. This would result in a lean mixture. To eliminate this leaning problem, additional ports, called *transfer ports*, are placed between the idle passage and the carburetor throat in the barrel just

above the throttle plate. At idle, these transfer ports act as additional air bleeds when they are exposed to atmospheric pressure above the closed throttle plate. As the throttle is opened, the transfer ports are exposed to high air velocity that flows around the throttle plate and to the manifold vacuum below it. The vacuum and velocity will draw fuel from the transfer ports as well as from the idle port, providing additional mixture necessary for transition from operation on the idle system to operation on the main system.

Power System. A larger volume of combustion charge is required to produce more power. Maximum power requires the charge to be a *rich* air/fuel mixture. Carburetors can be designed by correctly sizing fuel jets and air bleeds so that the main system will deliver air/fuel ratios for economy cruise conditions or for maximum power. Most carburetor main system air/fuel ratios are designed for economical cruising conditions, so they need a *power system* to provide the rich air/fuel ratio required at full throttle.

Power systems have a metering device that allows additional fuel to flow into the main well. The additional fuel raises the operating fuel level in the main well so that venturi vacuum will not have to lift the fuel as high. This higher fuel level allows more fuel to be discharged, thus producing a richer air/fuel mixture.

The power system is put into operation as the engine vacuum drops to a specified value, about five inches of mercury, or as the throttle is opened to a predetermined position, about sixty degrees. Carburetors often combine both vacuum and mech-

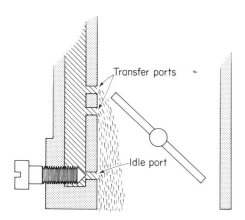

Fig. 5-16 Air and fuel flow during transition.

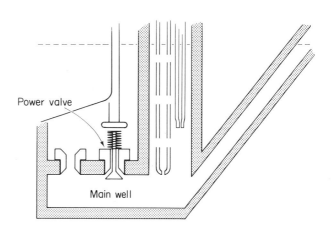

Fig. 5-17 Typical power valve.

anical sensing systems to operate the power jet. Many current model automotive carburetors use vacuum sensing alone; however, mechanical staging of the power system is now necessary on some carburetors to meet the critical emission standards of the Environmental Protection Agency.

Carburetors that have four barrels use two primary barrels during idle, transfer, and cruising conditions. Under power conditions, the secondary barrels are also opened to provide additional air/fuel mixture volume. These secondary barrels work along with the power system of the primary barrels to deliver an adequate quantity of combustion charge with the correct mixture for high power engine operation.

Acceleration Systems. At cruising speeds, fuel entering the cylinder is composed of vapors, atomized fuel, and liquid fuel. During low speed cruising operation, the engine runs with a high manifold vacuum and a reduced air flow. This running condition allows the manifold to become warm. The high vacuum and high temperature causes liquid fuel to completely evaporate, so that the manifold passages become dry.

When the throttle is suddenly opened, the first liquid fuel delivered will wet the manifold runner walls. Only the vapors and atomized fuel reach the cylinder. Since the fuel mass does not start to move as rapidly as air, the main system is slow to operate during sudden acceleration. These conditions produce a temporary leanness that will cause a misfiring often called *stumble*. Automotive carburetors are provided with an accelerating pump to inject additional fuel into the incoming air to compensate for this initial lean mixture.

An engine, represented by Figure 5-18, is to be accelerated from *A* to *D*. While running at point *A*, the accelerator is opened to provide wide open throttle (*WOT*). The acceleration pump supplies added fuel to bring the mixture up to point *B*. The power system carries the engine to point *C*, at which time the accelerator is reduced to road load cruising condition. The air/fuel curve returns to point *D*, which is the desired new road load condition.

The acceleration pump consists of an expanding and contracting chamber. The chamber is connected to the float bowl through an inlet check valve device. Its outlet is connected to an acceleration pump discharge nozzle through an outlet

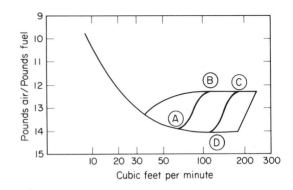

Fig. 5-18 Air/fuel ratio during acceleration from point A to point D.

check valve and passage. When the throttle is closed, the chamber expands. This pulls the outlet check valve onto its seat and pulls the inlet valve off its seat, allowing fuel to enter the chamber from the float bowl. When the throttle is opened, the inlet check valve is forced against its seat and the outlet check is forced off its seat, allowing fuel to be injected into the air stream through the acceleration pump discharge nozzle. Under steady-state engine operating conditions, the acceleration pump chamber is at rest and no fuel will flow. This requires a firm seating outlet check valve so that fuel is not pulled through the system by high velocity air flow. The pump chamber is kept full of liquid fuel by providing a small opening to allow fuel vapors to return to the float bowl.

Choke Circuit. Because of the low rate of fuel vaporization at low temperatures, the carburetor must deliver a very rich fuel mixture during a cold start so that there is sufficient fuel vapor avail-

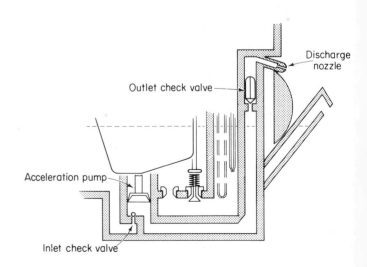

Fig. 5-19 Typical acceleration pump system.

able to produce a combustible mixture at the cylinders. The choke circuit in the carburetor provides this enrichment.

A choke plate is installed on a shaft in the air horn above the venturi. During cold starts, the choke is closed exposing the main discharge nozzle and idle ports to manifold vacuum. This pulls fuel from both systems until the mixture is rich enough to allow the engine to start. Two different methods may be used to close the choke prior to starting, a manual method and an automatic method. Most automotive carburetors use automatic chokes.

An automatic choke has a heat-sensing bimetallic spring that places a closing force on the choke linkages as the spring cools. When the driver is ready to start a cold engine, he depresses the accelerator, then removes his foot from the pedal. This releases the choke linkages and the choke immediately closes. The linkage is designed to keep the choke plate nearly closed until the engine starts. If some problem other than lack of fuel prevents the engine from starting, the engine will flood. To correct a flooded engine, the throttle linkage is provided with a device called an *unloader*, which opens the choke slightly when the throttle is fully opened.

As soon as the engine starts, it requires additional air and less fuel. This air is provided by partially opening the choke plate. Two forces are used to open the choke plate against the closing force of the bimetallic spring. First, the choke shaft is off-centered on the choke plate. This results in a velocity-sensing unbalanced force in the opening direction. The second force opposing the bimetallic spring is a vacuum-sensing, variable-displacement chamber that connects to the choke shaft through a linkage. Under light engine loads, high manifold vacuum provides a choke opening force through the vacuum chamber. Under heavy engine loads, manifold vacuum is low and the velocity high, so the offset choke plate forces the choke open. As the engine warms up, the bimetallic spring force gradually weakens, allowing the choke to be progressively opened while still maintaining a combustible air/fuel ratio. Because emission tests begin with a cold engine, the rich air/fuel mixture used during start and warmup contributes added emissions to the total emissions. Engine manufacturers have therefore designed the choke system to open as rapidly as possible. In some engines an electric heater is used to heat the choke spring to aid in rapid choke opening. Rapidly opening chokes often make the mixture so lean that the engine runs rough and the vehicle is hardly drivable. The idle enrichment system reduces this problem. Choke systems

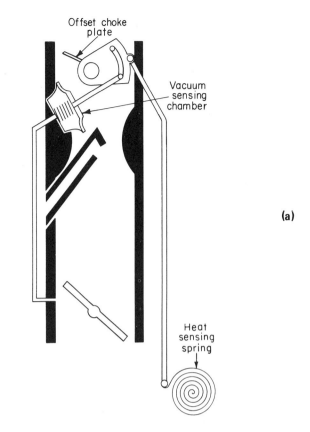

(a)

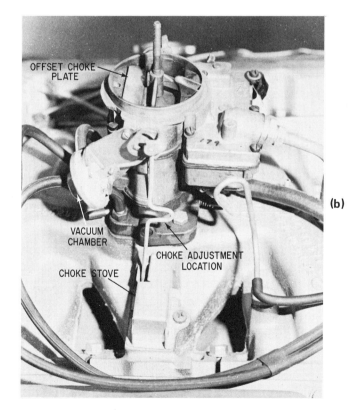

(b)

Fig. 5-20 Components of a typical choke system. (a) Section view of a typical cross over choke, (b) exterior view of typical choke parts.

MANIFOLD HEAT CHOKE STOVE

CONNECTION FOR ELECTRIC CHOKE HEAT

Fig. 5-21 Heating devices used on a typical integrated choke.

must be adjusted accurately to minimize customer complaints about drivability.

In a cold engine, the viscosity of the lubricating oil is high. More energy is required to keep a cold engine running, so the carburetor throttle plate must be opened more than is normally required by a warm engine at idle. Automotive carburetors are equipped with a *fast idle cam* that serves to hold the throttle partially open during warmup. The fast idle cam is operated by the choke through linkages. When the throttle is depressed on a cold engine, the spring closes the choke and this, in turn, pulls the fast idle cam into position. The cam will remain in the fast idle position as long as the throttle is not touched, even if the engine becomes warm and the choke opens completely. Some emission carburetors use a choke pulldown to force the choke open. When the automobile is driven during warmup, the fast idle cam will move to the correct position required for satisfactory idle speeds each time the throttle is opened. When the choke becomes fully open, the fast idle cam completely releases as the throttle is opened from its idle stop.

Return Check. Sudden throttle closing in some carburetor applications results in an abnormally high manifold vacuum. The light air quickly stops while the heavy fuel continues on toward the cylinder. In some engines this will cause a rich mixture that results in engine stall. A device called

(a)

(b)

Fig. 5-22 Fast idle cam. (a) Positioned for fast idle, (b) positioned for curb idle.

Fig. 5-23 Typical anti-stall dashpot or return check.

a return check or an anti-stall dashpot is used to eliminate this type of stalling problem. The return check is usually an air-vented diaphragm chamber or a fuel diaphragm that will catch the throttle linkage as it approaches its closed position. A vent in the diaphragm will dampen the throttle closing by gradually allowing the throttle to close against the stop under controlled conditions. Some return checks have manifold vacuum routed to one side of the diaphragm. When low manifold vacuum exists, a diaphragm spring moves the diaphragm and linkage to partly open the throttle. At high vacuum the diaphragm and spring are compressed to close the throttle to its idle stop. The rate of diaphragm movement is slowed by a restriction in the vacuum line to prevent engine stalling during deceleration. The return check is only used where carburetor-engine-vehicle combinations require its use.

REVIEW QUESTIONS

1. What is the carburetor designed to do?

2. Within a carburetor what is the name given to the difference in pressure used for sensing the power demand of the operator?

3. What is the name given to the fuel that is delivered to the air stream in small droplets?

4. What is the combustible air/fuel mixture range?

5. What is a stoichiometric mixture?

6. What mixture considerations are needed for maximum economy?

7. How do the mixture ratios supplied by a carburetor compare to those supplied by fuel injection?

8. Why is it helpful to have the fuel broken into small droplets?

9. When does the fast idle cam come into operation?

10. What establishes the base-line fuel pressure?

11. What controls fuel and air flow within a carburetor?

12. When is manifold vacuum high?

13. When is venturi vacuum high?

14. What is the purpose of the compensating device?

15. How does the main well perforated tube help carburetion?

16. When does the mechanical float-bowl vent open?

17. What is the function of the transfer ports at slow idle?

18. What is the name of a device that provides extra fuel as the throttle is moved from cruise to full throttle?

19. What device is used to eliminate stumble as the throttle is rapidly opened?

20. What is happening in the acceleration system as the engine runs at a steady cruising speed?

21. What force opens the choke as the engine idles?

22. What positions the fast idle cam?

51

6

Automotive Carburetors

Some engines can use one of several alternate makes of carburetors. Each carburetor used on an engine must supply the identical air/fuel mixture needed by that engine. Carburetor manufacturers use different construction details in the carburetor circuits to provide these identical mixtures.

Carburetor parts are made from a number of materials. Zinc and aluminum alloys are used for the main float bowl body and the air horn cover. Lower throttle bodies are made of aluminum or cast iron. Mineral-filled phenolic resin is used for a heat-insulating float bowl on some emission carburetors. Carburetor jets and internal rods are most often made of brass. Gaskets and seals are made from fuel-resistant fiber and synthetic rubber. Floats traditionally have had hollow sheet brass construction, but lightweight fuel-resistant plastic is gradually replacing brass as float material. Carburetor linkages and cams have been made of steel rods and stampings. Here again, some plastic parts are replacing metal parts.

There are a minimum number of standard carburetor body parts used in each carburetor model. Different size drilling and jetting can make these standard parts into carburetors that are adaptable to different individual engine requirements. This is why many carburetors look alike, but are not interchangeable between engine applications. Setting numbers stamped on carburetor parts or on tags attached to carburetors are the key to the specific jetting and engine application.

6-1 FLOAT AND NEEDLE VALVE

Carburetors use a float to establish the operating fuel level, called *wet fuel level*, by opening and closing a needle-type inlet valve on a valve seat. The inlet-valve tip is commonly made of a synthetic rubber-like elastomer material called Viton. The float must provide a force sufficient to close the valve against fuel pump pressure. Increases in fuel pump pressure will require a higher closing force to maintain the same wet fuel level. The closing force can be increased by submerging the float somewhat deeper. This is done by bending the float arms slightly. If the float mechanical position or *float level* is set without checking wet fuel level, it could actually lead to a high wet fuel level when fuel pump pressure is high or to a low wet fuel level when fuel pump pressure is low. A small spring pull-clip often connects the float arm and needle valve to aid in opening the float valve as the fuel level lowers.

Some carburetors have small float bowls and, consequently, small floats. The required float force alone is insufficient for adequate control, and so the float is aided by a spring, as shown in Figure 6-1 d. Another type uses a partially balanced inlet valve. In each of these systems, the float adds the small additional force required to close the valve on its seat against fuel pump pressure.

The foregoing discussion has ignored vehicle dynamics. During operation, an automobile will be

52

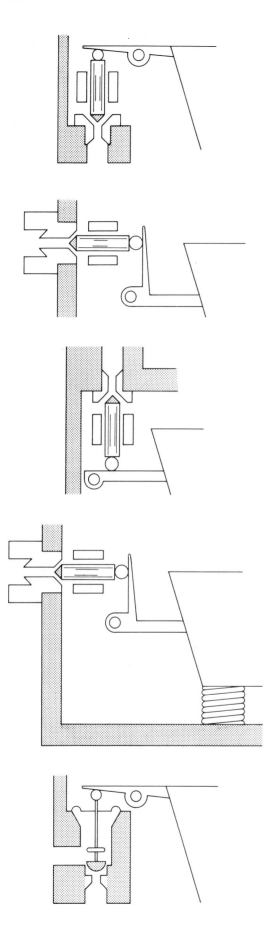

Fig. 6-1 Float bowl inlet valve types.

accelerated, decelerated, and turned rapidly. It will also go up and down hills, tilting the engine. Fuel in the float bowl acts as any liquid will in an enclosed container. During rapid acceleration, fuel will go to the back of the bowl. On braking, it goes to the front. On turns, it flows to the outside. The more violent the maneuver, the more the gasoline

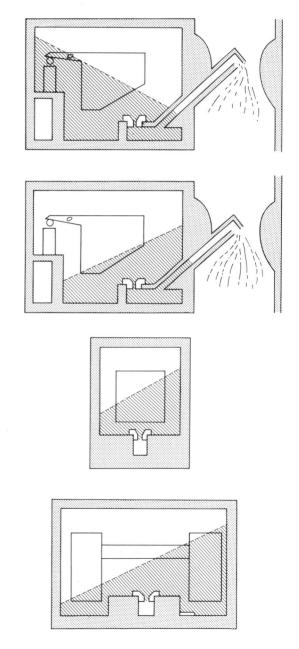

Fig. 6-2 Fuel action in the bowl as the vehicle is stopped quickly, accelerated rapidly, or turned violently.

moves. The carburetor is designed so that the main jets are not uncovered during these maneuvers. It is also designed so that the maneuvers do not flood the engine manifold by overflow from the main discharge nozzle. Floats and bowls are designed to minimize vehicle dynamic effects by centering the metering units and by providing multiple small metering units.

Single-barrel carburetors may have floats with either one or two pontoons. The float pontoons are usually placed at the side of the carburetor and are located as centrally fore and aft as possible. With a two pontoon float assembly, when the vehicle turns, one pontoon becomes nearly submerged and the other is nearly out of the fuel. This balances the force to maintain the correct wet fuel level above the main jet. Two-barrel carburetors usually have two pontoon float assemblies and operate in the same way as a single-barrel carburetor using a two-pontoon float assembly.

Four-barrel carburetors may have one float and float bowl or they may use a single float for the primary barrels and another float for the sec-

ondary barrels. Some carburetors use one float assembly to feed the primary and secondary pair on one side of the carburetor and another float assembly to feed the pair on the other side. Both single-pontoon and two-pontoon float assemblies are used. These may be located on the side of the carburetor or at front and rear. Another design uses a single, centrally located float bowl with a single-pontoon float assembly for both primary and secondary barrels. A small float bowl allows fuel to be controlled so that there is less chance of having the fuel uncover the jets during violent vehicle maneuvers. The small bowl will also produce less percolation vapor when the engine is turned off. This, in turn, minimizes hot start problems. A disadvantage of a small float bowl occurs when the warm engine is stopped and fuel in the bowl and fuel pump vaporizes. When one attempts to restart the engine, the fuel in the bowl is exhausted before fuel pressure can be reestablished to fill the bowl.

6-2 IDLE SYSTEM

The idle fuel delivery system is called the idle system. As mentioned in Chapter 5, the idle system takes fuel up through a passage, usually consisting

Fig. 6-3 Common carburetor barrel, float pontoon assembly, and float arrangements.

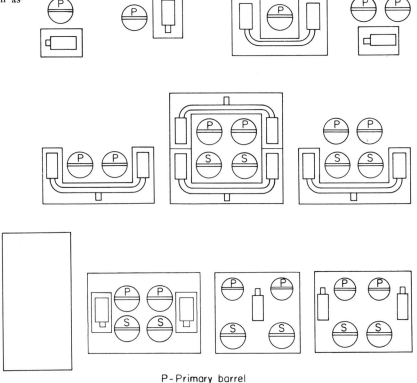

P - Primary barrel
S - Secondary barrel

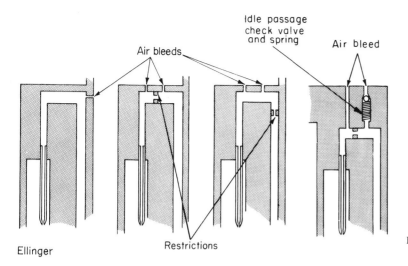

Idle passage
check valve
and spring

Air bleeds

Air bleed

Ellinger

Restrictions

Fig. 6-4 Typical idle air bleed arrangements.

of an idle tube with a restricting orifice or small metered opening at its lower end, to a passage above the fuel level where it meets an idle air bleed. Some carburetors have two idle air bleeds with a restriction between them to help meter idle fuel. The restriction is sometimes called an economizer. The fuel is led down a passage past transfer ports to the mixture screws and idle ports. Two-barrel carburetors have a complete separate idle system for each barrel. All four-barrel carburetors have idle systems in each of the primary barrels. Some four-barrel carburetors also have a secondary idle system to aid in transition as the secondary throttle plates open.

Idle air control is often neglected when the idle system is discussed. Most carburetors feed idle air around slightly open throttle plates. An idle

stop screw holds the throttle plate open sufficiently to allow the correct amount of air flow to maintain the correct idle speed. The idle stop screw is manually adjusted.

Some carburetor models use an air by-pass system to supply idle air. In these carburetors, the carburetor throttle plate is tightly closed. All of the idle air must enter the manifold through an air passage that is controlled with a large diameter adjusting screw. As the screw is loosened, more air is allowed to enter the manifold, thus increasing engine speed. Air adjustment must be synchronized with the idle mixture screw for correct idle speed and smooth operation.

During deceleration high manifold vacuum tends to pull excess fuel through the idle circuit. To prevent rich mixtures at high vacuum some

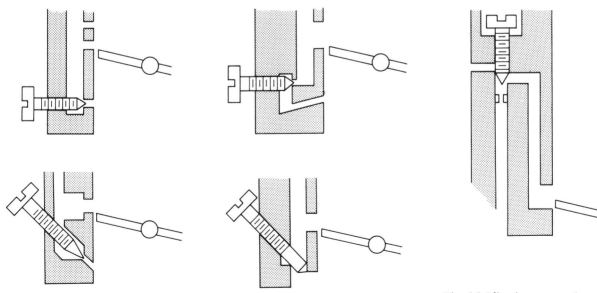

Fig. 6-5 Idle mixture control types.

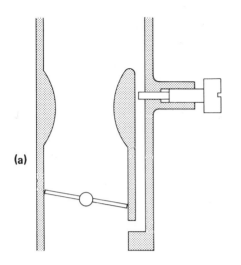

Fig. 6-6 Air bypass type idle speed adjustment. (a) Section view, (b) adjusting with a screwdriver.

emission control carburetors are equipped with a check valve above the idle passage on the downstream side of the idle restriction. When excess vacuum exists in the idle passage the check valve opens to allow extra air to bleed into the passage. With extra bleed air the idle system supplies a lean mixture to minimize rich deceleration mixtures.

Engines with high power loads at idle, such as air conditioning and power steering, become hot while idling. Engine heat soaks into the carburetor body and vaporizes some of the fuel from the float bowl. These vapors are led into the air horn through bowl vents where they are drawn back through the carburetor barrel with the incoming air. These va-

pors along with the normal idle fuel produce an over-rich mixture that is delivered to the manifold. To compensate for this condition, some carburetors are equipped with a *hot idle compensator*. It consists of a valve on a bimetallic spring. When the carburetor gets hot, the bimetallic spring opens an air passage, allowing air to by-pass the throttle plate to go into the manifold. This will lean the over-enriched mixture and increase engine speed. In this way the hot idle by-pass will compensate for the extra fuel vapors and for the added engine loads. When the carburetor cools, the bimetallic valve closes the port and the carburetor returns to normal idle conditions.

Fig. 6-7 Hot idle bypass arrangements. (a) Section view, (b) air horn location, (c) carburetor side location opened, (d) side location showing closing pin.

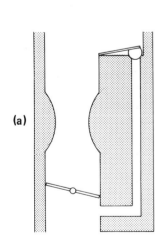
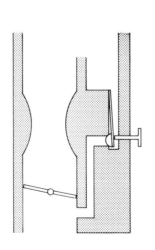

(c)

(d)

Care should be taken to see that the hot idle compensator is closed when the engine idle is set. In some cases, a small pin is provided to seat the idle compensator while the engine idle is adjusted.

6-3 MAIN AND COMPENSATION SYSTEM

The main and compensation system consists of a main jet, main well, discharge nozzle, and a compensating system.

The *main jet* is a threaded bushing having a carefully sized hole through the center. The holes in the jets are so critical in some models that they are individually checked on a flow calibrator before the jet number is stamped on them. They should not be prodded with a wire or be drilled. This will upset their carefully controlled calibration. In some exceptional cases manufacturers' service bulletins advise oversize drilling to correct an operational condition discovered after manufacturing.

The *main well* is a passage that is either die-cast or drilled in the carburetor body. It is on the downstream side of the main jet and encloses the main well vent tube as well as the idle tube. The discharge nozzle is on the extreme end of the main well, and may be a part of the body casting or it may be an added attachment part.

Many carburetors have a discharge cluster in which the discharge nozzle, much of the carburetor metering calibration (such as the air bleeds), the main well tube, perforated tube, and the idle tube are located. This discharge cluster fits on top of the main well with the tubes going into the main well.

Some carburetors use multiple venturis, one inside another, around the discharge nozzle to provide the required vacuum signal strength for use in air/fuel mixture control. The lower edge of each small venturi is located in the narrowest portion of the next larger venturi so that vacuum force is multiplied and the venturis are therefore often called *boost venturis*. This arrangement also provides a complete air curtain around the fuel being

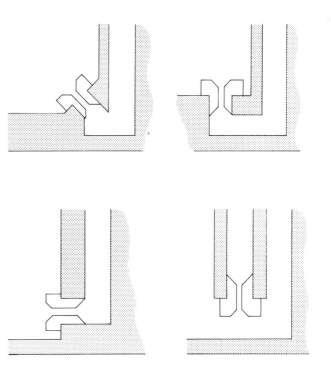

Fig. 6-8 Main jet arrangements.

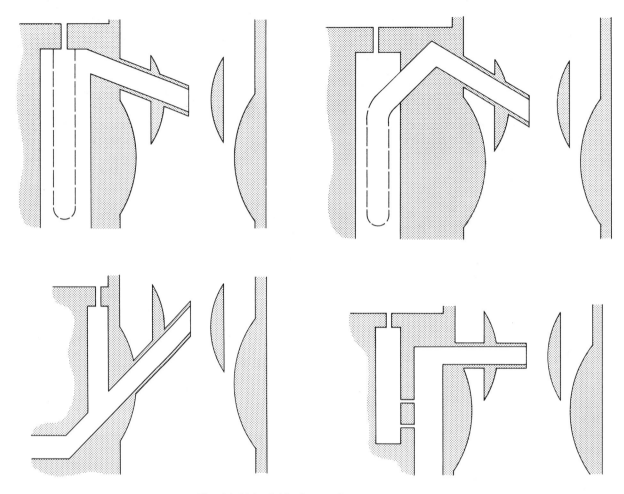

Fig. 6-9 Main air bleed vent tube arrangements.

Fig. 6-10 Typical discharge clusters.

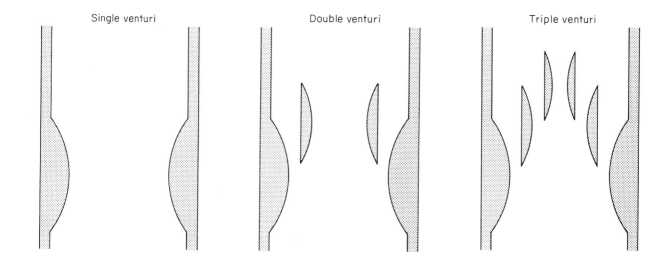

Single venturi   Double venturi   Triple venturi

Fig. 6-11 Common venturi arrangements.

discharged, so that it will thoroughly mix with the air. The extra venturis would reduce air flow at high engine speeds so they are made with a larger diameter to compensate for this.

The carburetor delivers fuel in proportion to air volume while the combustible air/fuel ratio is based on weight. Most automobile carburetors are calibrated to operate at 1000 feet (1.61 km) elevation. When an automobile is driven at sea level there is more air mass in each cubic foot of air consumed by the engine so the resulting mixture is lean. This provides poor drivability. In contrast to this, automobiles operated at several thousand feet above sea level use air having less mass per cubic foot. These engines operate rich and so they produce excess hydrocarbon and carbon monoxide emissions.

To compensate for the change in the air/fuel mixture with altitude some emission-control carburetors are equipped with altitude compensation. The altitude sensing device consists of an accordion shaped container which is sealed so no air can get in or out. This unit compresses as atmospheric pressure is exerted on it at sea level. It expands at less atmospheric pressure encountered at high elevation. A valve is positioned by the movement of one end of the atmospheric pressure-sensing unit. In one type the valve restricts the amount of air bleeding into the main well at sea level to enrich the mixture. It allows increasing quantities of air to bleed into the main well as the atmospheric pressure drops when the automobile operates at high elevations. This increase in bleed-air leans the mixture. In another type of altitude compensation the atmos-

pheric pressure-sensing unit moves a valve in a part-throttle jet. The sensing unit expands at high elevations pushing the valve into the jet to reduce the jet opening size. This reduces fuel flow into the main well to lean the mixture. Altitude compensation provides the automobile with low emissions and good drivability at all elevations.

6-4 POWER CIRCUIT

The power circuit comes into operation near full throttle. It consists of an engine power-sensing device and a method of adding about 15% more fuel to the main well than is possible through the main jet alone. This system is supplemented on four-barrel carburetors by providing for an additional quantity of rich air/fuel mixture to enter the manifold through secondary carburetor bores.

Throttle position was one of the first methods used to control the power circuit. It requires a *mechanical link* between the throttle and power mechanism. The setting of this link is critical for correct enrichment. As the throttle approaches a predetermined position, approximately 75% of full throttle, the linkage would start to mechanically open the fuel enriching device. The power device rapidly reaches full activation through link and bell crank geometry as the throttle is opened fully.

Under most operating conditions, *engine manifold vacuum* will more accurately sense engine power requirements than will throttle position. Engine manifold vacuum is a function of engine speed and throttle position. At high engine speed and part

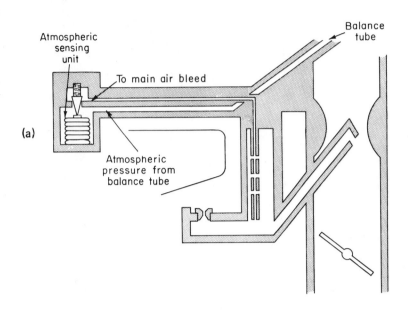

(a)

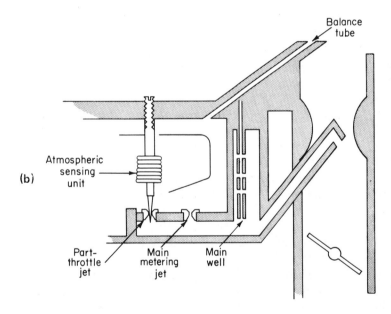

(b)

Fig. 6-12 Altitude compensation in the main air bleed. (a) Illustrates main air bleed restriction, (b) illustrates part throttle jet restriction.

throttle, such as operation at turnpike speeds, the manifold has a relatively high vacuum, from 14 to 16 inches (350 to 450 mm) of mercury (Hg). As the throttle is opened, manifold vacuum drops. The vacuum will be about 1 inch (25 mm) Hg when the throttle is fully open. Experience has shown that the power system should begin to enrich the mixture when manifold vacuum drops to 4 to 6 inches (100 to 150 mm) Hg.

A spring-loaded expanding chamber, either a diaphragm chamber or a piston in a cylinder, is used to sense engine vacuum and open the enriching device. Vacuum contracts the chamber against a calibrated spring. The calibrated spring expands the chamber when vacuum becomes too low to hold it compressed, thereby activating the enriching device.

The calibrated spring controls power-jet timing. There are no adjustments. Some carburetor models that are used for several different applications have a different calibrated spring strength for each application. Other carburetors use shims on

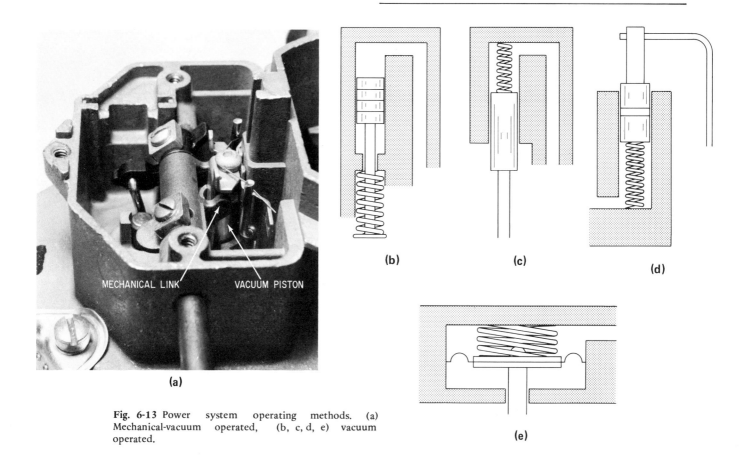

(a)

(b) (c) (d)

(e)

Fig. 6-13 Power system operating methods. (a) Mechanical-vacuum operated, (b, c, d, e) vacuum operated.

the spring seat to change the effective spring tension and, thus, the power valve timing may be set. There are no linkages to be accidentally bent out of alignment or to be adjusted. Most carburetors use the vacuum sensing method of power jet operation. Some carburetors in emission-controlled engines use a combination of both mechanical and vacuum methods to more fully cover engine requirements. The mechanical operation overrides the vacuum when required.

Two types of mixture enriching devices are used: *metering* or *step-up rods,* and *valves.* They are activated by one of the foregoing power-sensing devices. Both types of enriching devices allow more fuel to flow from the float bowl into the main well than can be supplied by the main jet alone, thus raising the fuel level in the main well. The higher fuel level reduces the distance the fuel must be raised to the discharge nozzle and, consequently, more fuel will be delivered. Added fuel will result in a richer air/fuel mixture as previously explained.

Metering rods or step-up rods extend through the main metering jet, one in each primary main jet. In lean cruising conditions, fuel goes through the annulus space formed between the jet hole and the rod. The rod has two or more different diameters, or it may have a taper. When the power-sensing device calls for a rich mixture, the rod is pulled upward so that the smaller diameter portion of the rod is in the main jet. This means that there is, in effect, a large main jet opening through which the fuel can flow, and thus the mixture is enriched. Some emission-control carburetors use a sealed calibration screw that limits the movement of the tapered metering rod to avoid excessive enrichment.

A single-barrel carburetor using the metering-rod enriching device has one main jet, one metering rod, and one actuating device. Two-barrel carburetors using metering rods use two main jets and two metering rods. There may be either one sensing device for both metering rods or a separate sensing device for each metering rod. Four-barrel carburetors have power systems on the primary

61

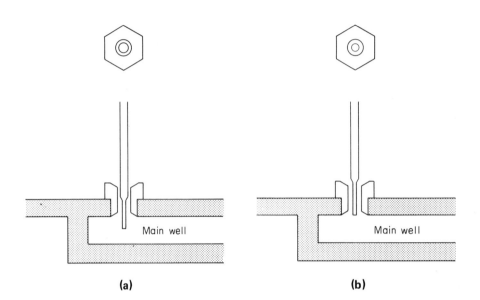

(a)   **(b)**

Fig. 6-14 Metering or step-up rods. (a) Rod in the main jet, (b) rod lifted from the main jet, (c) location of one type of factory adjustment metering rod limiter.

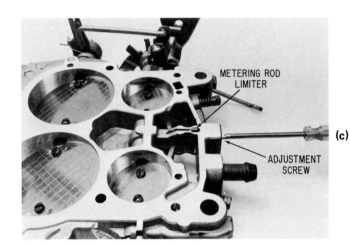

(c)

barrels and these operate in the same manner as those in two-barrel carburetors. In some four-barrel carburetors the metering rod is linked to an air valve that senses the air flow through the carburetor.

Power valves are used in many carburetors. The valve may be either a *poppet* valve or a *ball check* valve. This type of power system is always operated by a vacuum-sensing device. The valve remains closed under cruise conditions at high manifold vacuum. When manifold vacuum falls, a spring on the sensing control opens the power valve, either directly or through an actuating rod. This opens a passage that allows fuel to bypass the main jet to help fill the main well. A single by-pass valve is all that is required for single-barrel, two-barrel, or four-barrel carburetors.

The secondary barrels in four-barrel carburetors come into operation near wide-open throttle conditions when a large volume of rich air/fuel mixture is required and therefore the secondary barrels have normally rich carburetor jetting. They also use the same sensing signals that are used by the power system; that is, throttle position and vacuum.

Some four-barrel carburetors have a mechanical linkage between the primary and secondary throttle shafts. The secondary throttle plates start to open after the primary throttle plates have opened approximately 60 degrees. Both primary and

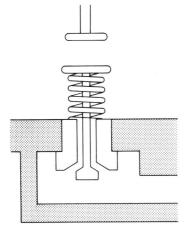

Poppet valve

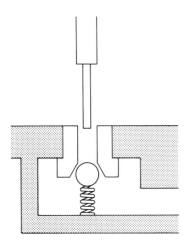

Ball check valve

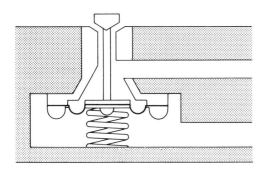

Poppet valve
diaphragm actuated

Fig. 6-15 Power system valves.

secondary throttle plates reach the wide-open position at the same time to allow maximum air flow at full throttle.

Mechanically controlled secondary barrels can be opened at full throttle and low engine rpm. A sudden opening will momentarily reduce air velocity through all the carburetor bores by allowing air to flow through the secondary bores. In many carburetors, this low velocity reduces primary venturi vacuum to the point that fuel will not flow from the primary main nozzle. When this happens, the engine gets a large quantity of lean mixture that causes the engine to misfire. An *air valve* or *velocity valve* in the secondary air horn is used to eliminate this type of lean mixture problem. The air valve shaft is offset to provide an unbalanced condition that will sense air flow. In static position, the unbalanced valve may be counterbalanced by a weight or torsion spring. When the secondary throttle is suddenly opened, the air valve stays closed until engine speed increases carburetor air velocity. Then, dynamic unbalance of the offset air valve allows the air valve to open gradually, while maintaining a pressure depression equivalent to about three inches (76 mm) of water. (Pressure expressed in terms of water is a more sensitive measurement than pressure expressed in inches of mercury.) The pressure depression or partial vacuum keeps the engine from getting a large amount of lean mixture at low engine speeds. As engine speed continues to increase, the air valve gradually opens, keeping the air/fuel mixture at a combustible ratio. Air valve opening may be dampened with a calibrated air bleed, a controlled-vacuum diaphragm chamber, or with a fuel damper chamber to eliminate the engine power *bog* or *sag* that would result from having the air valve open too quickly. Some carburetors use an air valve operated metering rod in the secondary main jets to control the mixture.

In some four-barrel carburetors, the secondary throttle plates are opened with a spring-loaded vacuum diaphragm that is linked to the secondary throttle shaft. The diaphragm is held by a calibrated spring in the direction that will keep the secondary throttle plates closed. As the primary throttle plates are opened, air velocity increases primary venturi vacuum. This vacuum applied to the vacuum chamber pulls the diaphragm against

63

(a)

(b)

(c)

(d)

(e)

Fig. 6-16 Mechanically operated secondary throttle valves. (a) Both throttles closed, (b) primary nearly open and secondary closed, (c) secondary starts to open as primary is opened further, (d) secondary fully open as primary becomes fully open, (e) one primary and one secondary barrel on a two-barrel carburetor used on a four-cylinder engine.

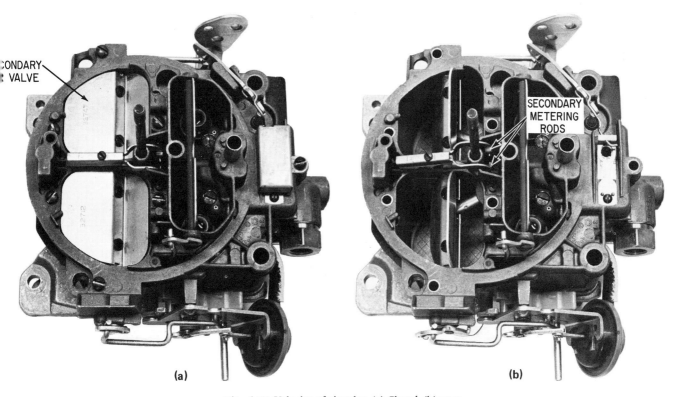

Fig. 6-17 Velocity of air valve. (a) Closed, (b) open.

the calibrated spring. The secondary throttles are opened with a linkage from this diaphragm movement. Secondary venturi vacuum is also used to pull the diaphragm so that the secondary throttle plates move rapidly once they start to open. This system of operation is very sensitive to actual engine requirements without the need to use a secondary air valve system.

Secondary throttle shafts are provided with a locking device that keeps the secondary throttle plates closed when the choke is applied. Only the primary barrels are equipped with a choke to provide rich mixtures during warmup. The engine would stall as a result of a lean mixture if the secondary throttles were opened while the engine still required partial choking.

Fig. 6-18 Mechanical linkage that opens the secondary throttle.

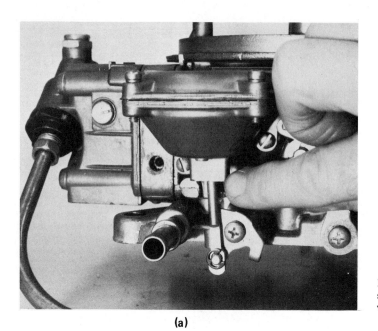

(a)

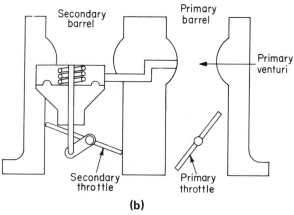

(b)

Fig. 6-19 Vacuum diaphragm opening mechanism for the secondary barrels. (a) Vacuum diaphragm linkage, (b) vacuum passage in the primary venturi.

6-5 ACCELERATION CIRCUIT

The acceleration circuit consists of a variable displacement chamber that senses fuel requirements; and an inlet check valve and an outlet check valve to supply fuel to a discharge nozzle. When the throttle is closed, fuel is drawn into the chamber from the float bowl through the inlet check valve. When the throttle is opened the fuel is forced out of the chamber through the outlet check valve and discharge nozzle.

The variable displacement chamber or pump may be either a piston in a cylinder or a diaphragm-sided chamber. When the throttle is closed, the chamber is expanded to draw fuel into the pump. This expansion may be controlled by a mechanical link from the throttle shaft or by high engine vacuum that is normal any time the engine is running at part throttle. When the linkage or engine vacuum releases the pump, the pump spring forces the chamber to contract and force fuel out. Pump spring action against the fuel provides the required fuel injection duration as fuel is forced from the discharge nozzle to wet the manifold. This provides the main system with needed time to begin functioning. Pump energy may be stored in the acceleration pump spring as the throttle is closed by the linkage or by vacuum. An alternate method

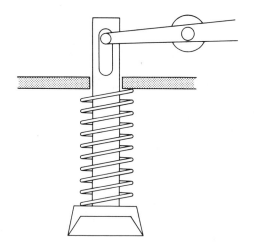

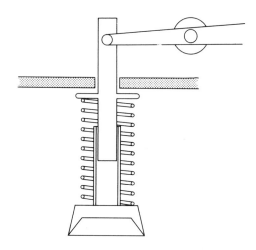

Fig. 6-20 Energy stored in an accelerator spring during closing and during opening.

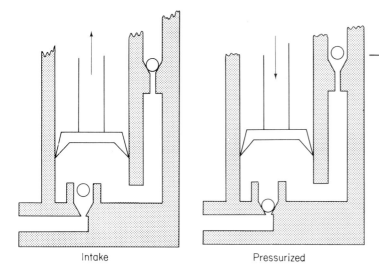

Fig. 6-21 Acceleration piston pump operation.

used on some mechanical linkages is to store the energy in the spring as the throttle is opened.

The acceleration pump inlet is located in a passage between the float bowl and the acceleration pump chamber. Sometimes, the valve is an inex-

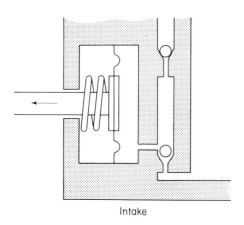

Intake

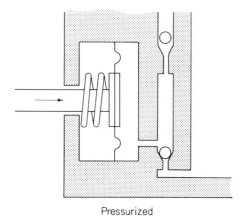

Pressurized

Fig. 6-22 Acceleration diaphragm pump operation.

pensive free floating ball. In other carburetors, the ball check valve is spring-loaded to insure positive seating. Another popular inlet check valve is an elastomer or fuel-resistant synthetic rubber disc over the inlet passage. The disc is lifted on the inlet stroke and compressed against the opening on the outlet stroke. Some acceleration pumps have an inlet check valve in the pump plunger shaft. This system works well because the entire pump is submerged within the fuel of the float bowl. A simple pump inlet valve method that is gaining popularity is to fit the pump plunger with a flexible loose fitting seal. On the upstroke, fuel enters the pump well around the seal and through the center hole of the seal. On the downstroke, the seal is forced against the solid portion of the pump plunger and pump chamber wall to seal the acceleration pump well.

The outlet check serves two functions. It keeps air from entering the pump chamber on the intake stroke and it keeps the outlet pump passage full of fuel, ready to be used at any instant. Here again, a ball check is popular. The ball check may be free-floating, spring-loaded, or weighted. Because the acceleration pump discharge nozzle is often in high velocity air, there may be sufficient suction to cause the outlet check to leak. To prevent this in some carburetors, the outlet check valve is weighted to prevent leakage. Some carburetors use a heavy outlet needle valve rather than the lightweight ball-type check valve.

Many acceleration pump chambers have an auxiliary opening in the acceleration system to vent vapors from the chamber. This may be a very small hole in the upper portion of the pressure chamber or it may be a check ball in the pump plunger. If the vapors were not allowed to vent from the fuel

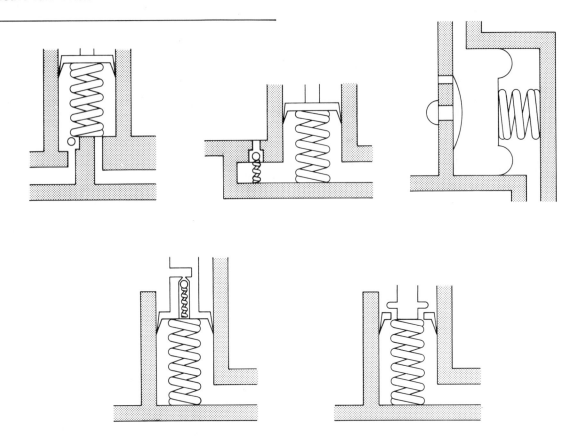

Fig. 6-23 Acceleration pump inlet check valve types.

(a)

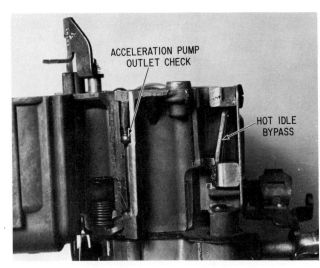

(b)

Fig. 6-24 Pump check valves. (a) Elastomer inlet check valve, (b) spring loaded ball outlet check.

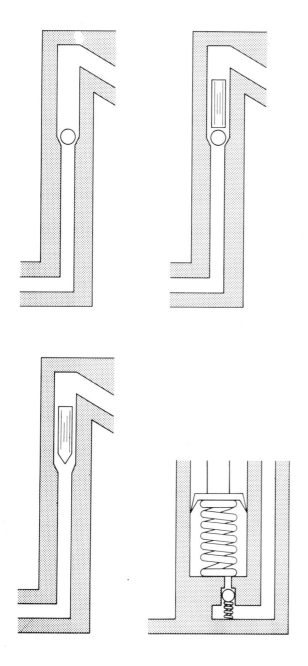

Fig. 6-25 Acceleration outlet check valves.

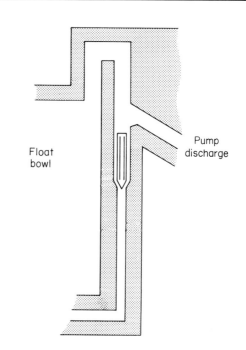

Fig. 6-26 Acceleration pump vent and overflow return.

chamber they would push fuel from the acceleration pump outlet when the engine was not running. This would lead to hot start problems.

The acceleration pump discharge nozzle sprays its charge into the air stream at each primary barrel. The quantity must be correct for each specific engine application. Discharge quantity is controlled by the acceleration pump spring calibration, the linkage adjustment, and the discharge nozzle opening size. Because standard carburetor castings and linkages are used for a number of engine applications, some acceleration pumps will provide more

fuel than the engine requires so these carburetors are provided with an opening, leading from the passage between the outlet check and the discharge nozzle to the top of the float bowl, that will allow excess fuel and vapors to return to the float bowl.

6-6 AUTOMATIC CHOKE CIRCUIT

Two forces balance to produce the correct choke opening. A temperature sensing bimetallic spring provides a closing force. Engine vacuum, along with an unbalanced choke plate, provides an opening force.

The bimetallic heat sensing spring in some carburetors is located integrally with the choke shaft on the carburetor air horn. Heat is piped to this type of bimetallic spring from a choke stove located where it is exposed to exhaust heat, such as in the exhaust manifold or in the exhaust cross-over in the intake manifold. Other designs place the bimetallic spring in a pocket or well cast on the outside of the manifold where it can be directly exposed to exhaust heat. Some emission-control carburetors have an electric heating coil placed in the choke well with the bimetallic spring, to aid in rapid choke opening. The spring is connected to the choke shaft by a cross-over link.

CHOKE SPRING AND
VACUUM PISTON
HOUSING

FAST IDLE CAM

UNLOADER TANG

CHOKE HEAT STOVE

(a)

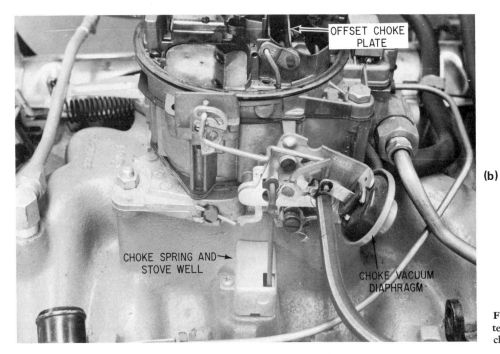

OFFSET CHOKE
PLATE

CHOKE SPRING AND
STOVE WELL

CHOKE VACUUM
DIAPHRAGM

(b)

Fig. 6-27 Choke spring types. (a) Integral choke spring, (b) cross-over choke with the spring in a choke well.

Engine vacuum sensing force is applied to the choke shaft through a link between the shaft and a vacuum piston or a vacuum diaphragm. This vacuum force tends to pull the choke open against the bimetallic spring force. The tendency of choke vacuum pistons to gum up and stick in their bores has led to the widespread use of the vacuum diaphragm opening method.

6-7 CARBURETOR ICING

Heat is required to evaporate fuel as it flows through the carburetor. Much of the heat is removed from the air itself, thus lowering the air temperature. If the air is cooled below the temperature at which the moisture in the air condenses, called the dew point, moisture from the air will collect on the

70

Fig. 6-28 Electrically heated choke spring.

Fig. 6-29 Choke opening piston (left) and choke opening diaphragm (right).

throttle plate and surrounding carburetor area. If this temperature is below 32°F (0°C) the moisture will freeze, causing ice to form in the throttle plate area of the carburetor. Ice that forms will block the transfer passages and effectively change the shape of the carburetor bore. This upsets carburetor calibration, enriching the mixture and stalling the engine.

Icing will most likely occur when there is high humidity and the temperatures are between 30° and 50°F (-1° and 10°C). When the engine first starts, no problem will be noticed because the ice has not had time to build up. When the engine is warm, the carburetor parts are above the freezing

temperature so ice will not form. Carburetor icing occurs during the warmup period after the engine has run at light loads for about five minutes. It occurs quicker with slight throttle openings than with greater throttle openings. Engines that are sensitive to carburetor icing often have their idle mixture adjusted to the lean side and have idle set at the maximum specified idle speed.

In modern emission control systems the air is pre-heated before it enters the carburetor, effectively eliminating carburetor icing problems. Some manifolds are designed to direct exhaust gas against the carburetor base by making a bypass in the manifold crossover. This is designed to minimize carburetor icing at idle.

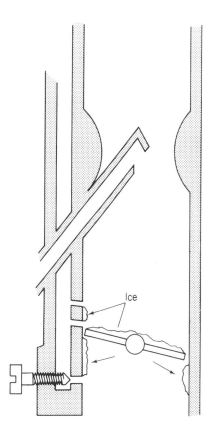

Fig. 6-30 Carburetor icing location.

REVIEW QUESTIONS

1. Why should carburetors that look alike not be interchanged?

2. With the float level set properly what will an increase in fuel pump pressure do to carburetion?

3. What is the advantage of a two-pontoon float assembly?

4. Why do some four-barrel carburetors have an idle system in the secondary side?

5. What controls idle speed?

6. What carburetor device prevents overrich operation on an engine that encounters excessive heat while idling?

7. What is the purpose of multiple venturis?

8. What happens to manifold vacuum as the throttle opens?

9. What happens to the venturi vacuum as the throttle is opened?

10. What activates the power enrichment system?

11. Where do the vacuum operated secondary throttles pick up the vacuum opening signal?

12. Why are air valves used in secondary barrels?

13. How do mechanically operated secondary throttle plates compensate for full throttle mixture leaning when the engine is cold?

14. Why is the acceleration pump outlet check valve relatively heavy?

15. When does a carburetor tend to form ice?

7

Carburetor Service

Carburetors should not be serviced for other than routine idle adjustments until an engine operation problem is positively identified as a carburetor problem. This means that when an engine is malfunctioning all other engine systems should be checked for correct operation before the carburetor is condemned. Carburetor problems usually show up as a flooding condition, malfunctioning choke, severe backfiring, sticking throttle, inability to set idle, or no acceleration-pump action. On emission-controlled engines, surge-type and roughness-type drivability problems may be due to lean carburetor mixtures. Excessive carbon monoxide in the exhaust indicates a carburetor problem.

Many carburetor problems occur when a technician improperly services the carburetor. Such problems are usually a result of incorrect cleaning methods, improperly torqued assembly screws, incorrect part assembly, or use of the wrong parts. All carburetor parts must be handled with care to avoid damage, and they must be kept clean. Jets should only be cleaned with solvents and air pressure. Do not push wires through carburetor jet holes; this will scratch their inner surface and change their calibration, and so the carburetor will not meter fuel correctly and the engine will not operate properly.

Carburetor service usually involves completely disassembling the carburetor; cleaning metal parts in a good carburetor solvent; rinsing them; and drying them with compressed air. Parts are in-

spected to see that they are in normal condition. The carburetor is reassembled with required replacement parts. New gaskets and seals should always be used. During assembly, carburetor settings must be checked and adjusted as necessary. The specifications and specific checking methods, as well as adjustment procedures, may be found in the service manual that covers the specific carburetor being serviced.

7-1 CARBURETOR EXTERNAL ADJUSTMENTS

The most common carburetor adjustment is engine idle. It essentially involves setting the idle mixture screw to provide a smooth idle and setting the idle speed screw to give the specified idle speed on a warm engine. Emission-control carburetors have limiters that prevent excessively rich idle adjustments and therefore it may be impossible to adjust them rich enough to provide as smooth an idle as desired. Before idle adjustment is attempted, all engine systems should be functioning correctly and the engine should be operated long enough to become sufficiently warm so that the choke will fully open and release the fast idle cam.

Positive Crankcase Ventilation. Before idle adjustment is attempted the positive crankcase ventilation (PCV) system must function correctly.

The PCV valve can be checked by slipping it from the engine. Shaking the valve will cause it to rattle if the valve is moving freely in its case. The PCV hoses should be in good condition and should be attached correctly. A normally operating PCV system allows some crankcase vapors with air to enter the intake manifold. When the PCV hose is pinched closed, vapors will stop flowing through the PCV system into the manifold. This will reduce idle speed over 50 rpm. If the engine speed does not drop, the PCV system is plugged and should be serviced. The PCV problem will be either a stuck valve or plugged hoses. The PCV can also be checked with a hydrocarbon tester as described in a later section.

Curb Idle. Other conditions must be met before curb idle can be correctly adjusted. Depending on the engine make and model these conditions include having correct ignition timing; placing the transmission in neutral with the parking brake set; turning the headlights on; turning the air conditioning on; removing the vapor vent line; and removing the distributor vacuum line and then plugging it while the idle adjustment is being made. Applicable conditions are usually indicated on a sticker located on the inside fender pan, on a radiator support, or on the inside of the hood within the engine compartment. Idle is adjusted with the air cleaner installed and other vacuum hoses connected in their normal position. When the conditions that apply are met, the engine curb idle can be correctly set.

Idle settings involve two adjustments, an air adjustment that primarily controls idle speed and a mixture adjustment that controls idle smoothness. Idle *speed* is adjusted by one of two methods. The most common speed adjustment method is to limit throttle plate closing with a throttle stop screw located on the carburetor linkage. Air going around the slightly open throttle plate supplies air required for engine idle. A second method used on a few carburetor models to provide idle air is to completely close the throttle plate and to supply the air through a bypass passage in the carburetor body. The passage opening size is adjusted by a large idle-air adjusting screw protruding into the passage. Increasing air flow into the engine by either method will increase engine speed. Idle *mixture* is controlled by idle needle screws usually located near the base of the carburetor. In some carburetor models this screw is located in the idle air-bleed passage. The screws control the amount of fuel delivered through the carburetor idle system to the incoming air. Emission-control carburetors have limiters sealed in the idle circuit that prevent excessively rich idle mixtures. The adjustable mixture screws can lean the mixture from this preset rich mixture point. In most carburetor models an idle mixture screw is provided for each carburetor primary barrel. Some carburetors, however, are designed to use a single mixture screw to control the mixture on two primary barrels.

Curb idle is adjusted by first adjusting the idle mixture screws, within the range of the limiter stops, to make the engine run smoothly at the high-

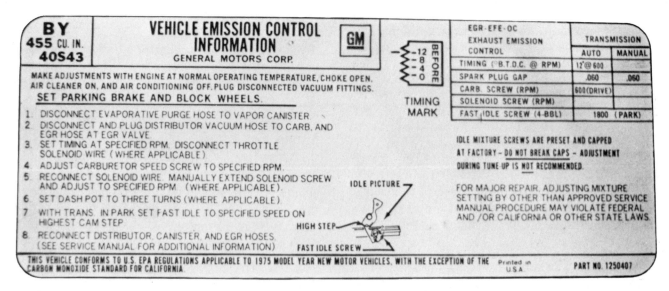

Fig. 7-1 Engine compartment sticker.

Fig. 7-2. Curb idle speed adjustment locations, (a)-(i).

(a)

(b)

(c)

(d)

(e)

(f)

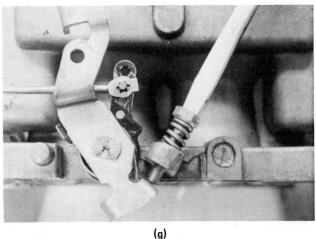

(g)

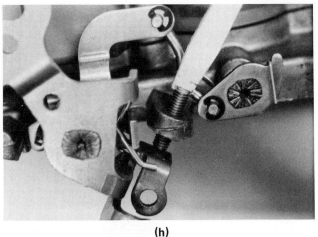

(h)

(i)

est rpm. High vacuum gauge readings and tachometer readings help determine this point. Some manufacturers also recommend the use of an exhaust gas analyzer or hydrocarbon-carbon monoxide tester when setting idle. *Each* mixture screw should be turned 1/16 of a turn at a time, alternating between screws and allowing about 10 seconds for the engine speed to stabilize before making the next adjustment. Idle mixture is adjusted by turning the idle mixture screws clockwise to lean the mixture until the engine begins to slow down, then turning them counterclockwise to enrich the mixture. This should cause the engine to begin to speed up again. Continued turning counterclockwise will again slow the engine speed when the screws are turned too far. Some idle screws have an internal limit-stop that will cause the screw to break if the technician tries to force it. The screws are readjusted to the point where the engine will idle smoothly at the highest speed. Idle mixture adjustment is done on each mixture screw turning

each the same degree. If turning the mixture screws has no effect on engine idle, the idle system is malfunctioning. To correct this condition, the carburetor will have to be opened and the idle system cleaned to give proper operation. If the engine does not run smoothly when it is adjusted within the range of the idle mixture limiters then the external limiter stops, when used, can be removed allowing the idle mixture to be adjusted further to give the smoothest and fastest possible idle. Some states have laws that allow only technicians with licenses for emission-control service to remove the limiter caps and make the adjustments using an exhaust-gas analyzer or hydrocarbon-carbon monoxide tester.

With the engine running smoothly, idle speed is set by turning the throttle stop screw or air screw to provide the specific engine idle speed. In some model emission-control carburetors the idle speed is set by making an adjustment on an idle-stop solenoid. The mixture screw setting should be re-

Fig. 7-3. Idle mixture adjustment locations, (a)-(e).

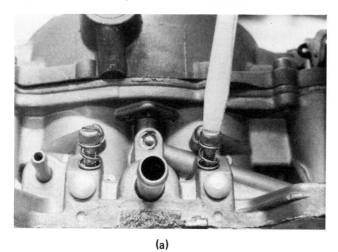

(a)

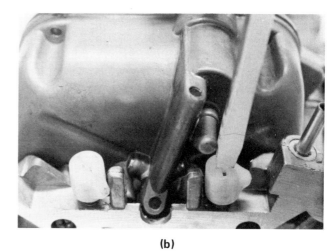

(b)

(c)

(d)

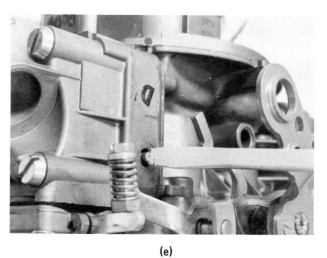

(e)

checked after the idle speed has been set to make sure it is still at the best mixture setting.

Emission-control carburetors are adjusted lean to help keep exhaust emissions low. It is best when adjusting curb idle to use an exhaust-gas analyzer or a hydrocarbon-carbon monoxide (HC-CO) tester. The idle mixture screw is adjusted to give as smooth an idle as possible while keeping the meter reading below the maximum rich mixture specification, approximately 14:1 air/fuel ratio or less than 1% CO on emission-control carburetors. If the idle mixture limiter stops were removed during idle adjustment they should be replaced with colored replacement-type mixture limiter stops.

An idle adjustment procedure is given by some manufacturers for use on emission-controlled engines when an exhaust-gas analyzer or HC-CO tester is not available. This method follows the normal idle adjustment procedure as previously described but also involves setting the idle speed at about 75 rpm above specified idle speed. After this adjustment is made, correct curb idle speed and emission mixture are obtained by further leaning the mixture screws equally, 1/16 turn at a time, without touching the speed screws. Alternate adjustments between mixture screws when more than one mixture screw is used until the correct idle speed is obtained. This leans the idle mixture, slowing the engine.

This adjustment will cause the mixture to fall into the emission specification range. Specific idle adjustment procedures are given on the tune-up decal placed in the engine compartment.

It might be noted here that during calibration of school instruments for the Plymouth Trouble Shooting Contest the author has frequently found the instruments used by schools to be incorrect. Tachometers have been as much as 200 rpm incorrect and dwell meters 5 degrees incorrect. Instruments this far off from calibration are worse than useless for adjusting modern emission-controlled engines. It is a good practice to have instruments calibrated at regular intervals.

Linkage Adjustment. Other external carburetor controls are positioned by linkages. Linkage adjustments can be made on the carburetor without disassembly when it is off the engine. Many of the adjustments can be made while the carburetor remains installed on the engine. The linkages seldom have to be adjusted unless someone has tried to correct carburetor operation by bending the linkages or unless the carburetor has been in an accident. All carburetor linkages must move freely with no binding. They operate without lubrication. Lubrication would collect dirt which will generally cause the linkages to stick and wear.

Each carburetor make, model, and application has its own specific linkage adjustment. The name of the carburetor make is cast on its exterior surface. For each carburetor make there are a number of carburetor models. Sometimes the model

Fig. 7-4 Setting number identification tag on a carburetor bowl screw.

(a)

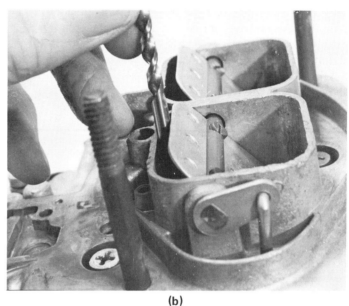

(b)

Fig. 7-5 Methods of measuring linkages. (a) Scale, (b) gauge.

identification is cast on the exterior. Most models are quite different so it is easy to identify carburetor models with illustrations of carburetors in reference books. A single model of a carburetor may be used on a large number of different engine types requiring different metering and different operating linkages. Numbers and letters stamped on the carburetor or on an attached tag give the carburetor setting number. The setting number is used to specify the specific carburetor-engine combination. Details of linkage adjustments for all carburetor makes, models, and settings are beyond the scope of this book. Service manuals and instruction sheets accompanying repair parts kits that apply to the specific engine and carburetor will have to be consulted for accurate carburetor adjustment. General linkage adjustment procedures will be discussed.

A common linkage adjustment method is to move one end of the link to an extreme position, then measure the position or the amount of travel at the other end of the link. Measurement may be made with a scale, a numbered drill shank, or a special gauge. A second method of linkage adjust-

ment is to move the operating members on each end of linkage to one of their extreme positions. The linkage should then drop into place or match a notch or an indicating mark. Still another method is to measure the length of the linkage directly. If the linkage is incorrect it can be bent at points pro-

Fig. 7-6 Typical linkage adjustment bending method.

vided in the link to give the correct linkage adjustment. After adjustment, the linkage should be rechecked to see that it operates freely.

Linkages are held on the carburetor by the way they are bent, by an upset tang, with cotter pins, with an E ring, with special spring-type carburetor clips or by screws or nuts. During carburetor service the special clips often fly off and are lost unless the technician takes special care to hold them as they are removed. It is usually difficult to find the correct replacement for lost clips.

Bowl Vent. Carburetor bowls have special vents that open to allow pressure from gasoline vapors to escape from the carburetor when the engine is stopped. If the vapors were trapped in the float bowl they would force liquid fuel from the discharge nozzle into the manifold. This type of action is called *percolation*. The bowl vent allows the vapors to escape, leaving liquid fuel in the carburetor bowl. In emission-controlled cars, the carburetor bowl vapors are directed to a *canister* that traps vapors; in non-emission-controlled cars vapors vent directly to the atmosphere.

The bowl vent adjustment is checked with the throttle closed and the engine off. If the vent opening is incorrect, its operating linkage can be adjusted to provide the proper amount of vent opening.

Fast Idle. Fast idle settings can be made while the carburetor is off the engine as well as when it is on the engine. The usual procedure when checking fast idle with the carburetor off the engine is to place a specific size drill bit shank or gauging tool between the throttle plate and carburetor bore. With the throttle plate closed against the gauge and the choke fully closed, the idle speed screw is adjusted to touch the choke-controlled fast idle cam at a specified point. To find this point on some carburetors it may be necessary to place a drill bit shank or gauging tool between the choke plate and carburetor bore. Fast idle can also be checked and adjusted on a running engine. The adjustment is made on a warm engine. The fast idle cam is positioned so the fast-idle stop screw is resting on a specified step of the fast idle cam. This position may require gauging the amount of choke plate opening setting. If positioning specifies the low cam step, the engine speed will be near 1000 rpm. If it specifies the high step the speed will be over 2000 rpm.

(a)

(b)

Fig. 7-7 Bowl vents. (a) Atmospheric, (b) vent to canister.

On some emission-control carburetors it may be necessary to disconnect some of the emission controls during fast idle adjustment. In general the emission controls must be made to operate as they would if the engine were cold. It is necessary to follow specific carburetor-engine instructions because there are so many different combinations used in modern emission-control systems.

Unloader. The choke is closed while the engine is cranking. If the engine does not immediately start, because of weak ignition, for example, the engine will pull too much fuel into the manifold causing an over-rich or flooded condition. Carburetors are provided with an unloader to overcome this condition. The unloader is a tab or tang on the throttle control lever that contacts the fast idle cam when the throttle is fully opened. This moves the cam, which in turn pulls the choke plate par-

Fig. 7-8 Fast idle speed adjustments.

tially open through the fast idle linkage. The amount of choke plate opening is measured with a drill bit shank or gauge between the choke plate and carburetor bore. If the opening is incorrect the tab or tang on the throttle control lever can be bent to give the proper choke opening.

Acceleration Pump. A linkage from the throttle control lever is used to mechanically operate the acceleration pump. When the throttle is closed the acceleration pump fills. Opening the throttle pushes fuel from the acceleration pump discharge nozzle. Two points are critical on the acceleration pump linkage adjustment. The pump must be in the correct starting position to make sure it will be able to deliver a full fuel charge. This is usually checked by measuring the distance between the pump end of the linkage and a fixed point on the carburetor. This distance is correctly positioned by bending the link or by adjusting a screw position between the throttle control lever and the

pump. A second adjustment that needs to be checked is the acceleration pump stroke. Pump stroke is the measured distance the pump travels from closed throttle to fully open throttle. If it is incorrect most acceleration pump linkages are provided with several different linkage position holes for longer or shorter pump strokes.

Choke. The automatic choke heat-sensitive thermostatic spring may be built integral with the carburetor or it may be fastened at the manifold using a cross-over link to connect to the carburetor choke lever. When the thermostatic spring is integral it has an insulated heat tube running between a manifold heat stove and the choke spring housing. Engine vacuum, pulling on an internal vacuum choke piston or through a special passage in the choke spring housing, draws fresh air through the choke stove where it is warmed by exhaust heat. The warmed air flows through the insulated tube to the choke spring housing so the spring can sense en-

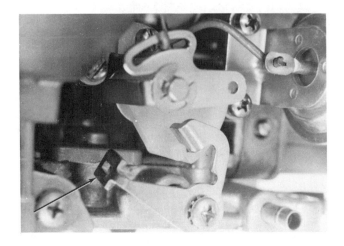

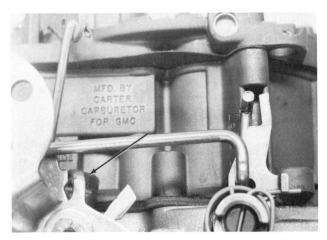

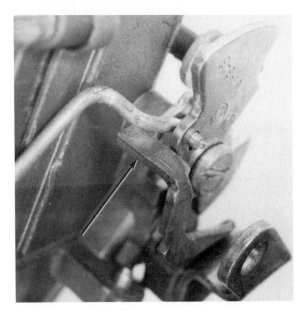

Fig. 7-9 Unloader adjustments.

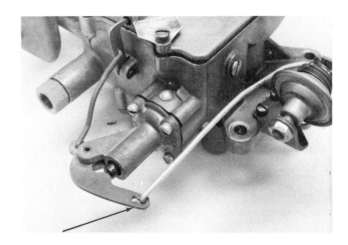

Fig. 7-10 Acceleration pump linkage adjustments.

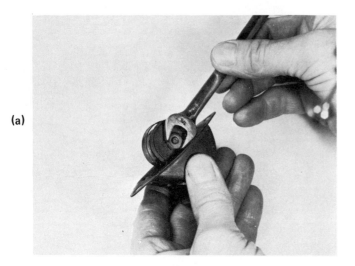

(a)

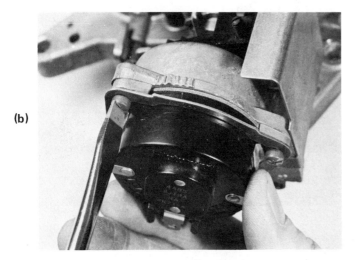

(b)

Fig. 7-11 Choke adjustments. (a) Cross-over well type, (b) integral type.

gine temperature. Some integral choke springs are warmed with an engine coolant passage or an electric heating coil that turns on with the ignition. As the engine coolant or electric heater becomes warm it heats the choke spring to allow choke opening.

When the thermostatic coil spring is not directly on the choke shaft it is connected to the choke shaft by an adjustable linkage. For adjusting, the choke spring is positioned or is held against its closed extreme limit and the link length is adjusted to give proper choke plate closing tension. Service manuals should be consulted for specific

adjustments when the choke does not function correctly.

Vacuum applied to the choke piston or diaphragm opens the choke. When a piston is used it is usually located in the choke thermostatic spring housing on a link attached to the choke shaft. It is seldom adjustable and it must move freely. The vacuum diaphragm, sometimes called a *choke breaker* or *vacuum kick*, is mounted independently from the thermostatic spring and is connected to the choke operating arm by a link. It is adjusted by retracting the vacuum diaphragm fully with an external vacuum source or by hand, then adjusting the link to give the specific amount of choke opening. The amount of choke opening is measured with a drill bit shank or a gauge.

(a)

(b)

Fig. 7-12 Choke opening vacuum diaphragm. (a) Measuring, (b) adjusting.

An improperly operating choke breaker or vacuum kick will cause engine performance problems during warmup with the mixture being either too rich or too lean, depending on the specific fault. This may be the result of bent linkages, improperly set choke opening, leaking diaphragm, or leaking vacuum hoses.

The thermostatic choke springs that are remotely mounted in a manifold well are set for the specific carburetor model used. They are not ordinarily designed for adjustment. Integral thermostatic coil choke springs are adjusted by turning the spring housing cover in the direction which will close the choke plate. At this point alignment notches on the choke housing and cover are visible. The choke should be set to the specified number of rich or lean notches.

Secondary Throttle. Secondary throttles should start to open after the primary throttles are about two-thirds open. Mechanically operated secondary throttle linkages are checked by opening the primary throttle plates a measured amount. At this point the secondary throttle plates should start to open when the choke is open. Early model carburetors with vacuum-operated secondary throttles have an adjustable stop screw that requires positioning. Late model carburetors do not require adjustment on vacuum-operated secondary throttles.

Some carburetors with mechanically operated secondary throttles use air valves above the discharge cluster. The air valve may be held closed with a balance weight or with spring tension. The balance weight closing requires no adjustment. The spring closure type must be adjusted. To do this

(a)

(b)

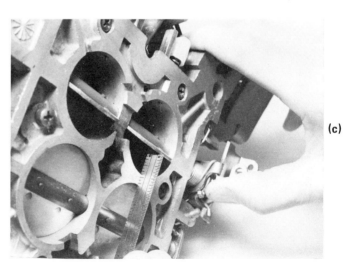

(c)

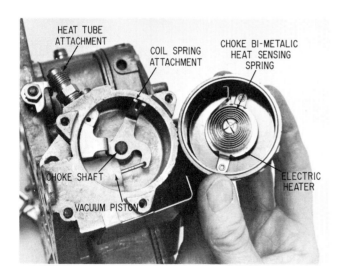

Fig. 7-13 Internal parts of an integral type choke.

Fig. 7-14 Secondary throttle adjustments. (a) Vacuum operated, (b) mechanically operated, (c) measurement of primary opening at the point the secondary is ready to open.

the spring tension is released until the air valve is open. The spring tension then is gradually tightened until the air valve just closes. The spring is tightened still further, approximately two turns, to give the air valve the correct closing tension for normal operation.

The preceding adjustments are the ones most commonly found in modern carburetors. Some additional specific adjustments may be found on some carburetors. These are described in service manuals and on instruction sheets that are included with carburetor repair kits.

7-2 MINOR CARBURETOR SERVICE

A carburetor needs additional service when all of its external adjustments are correctly set and the carburetor still does not function correctly. A number of things can be done to the carburetor without removing it from the engine. These will be called minor service.

Bowl Cover. The carburetor bowl cover can be removed from most carburetors while the carburetor is still installed on the engine. (Some models of Holley carburetors are an exception.) This eliminates the need to remove the throttle linkages and a number of hoses. To remove the bowl cover the choke cross-over link or choke heat tube is disconnected. The accelerator pump link is removed and

(a)

Fig. 7-16 Lifting a bowl cover from a carburetor.

(b)

Fig. 7-15 Secondary barrel air valve. (a) Held open, (b) closed with a spring.

the vacuum-kick link or hose is disconnected. These are included on most carburetors but some will also have step-up rods, a secondary metering rod, and a fuel line that must be removed to free the bowl cover. The hold-down screws are then removed and the bowl cover is lifted straight up. If the bowl cover does not come off freely, recheck to make sure that all attachments have been properly disconnected. Forcing will only damage the carburetor. When the bowl cover is removed most of the internal carburetor working parts are visible.

Internal Service. The metering parts of the carburetor may be suspended from the bowl cover or they may be attached directly in the bowl. In some carburetors metering parts are split, some

Fig. 7-17 Carburetor jetting in the bowl.

Fig. 7-19 Lifting the float with the hinge pin and needle valve.

being attached to the bowl cover and others attached in the bowl. In any case they can be removed for examination and cleaning.

With the bowl cover removed, examine the deposits in the bottom of the float bowl. The float bowl should be clean and free from foreign material. Often small rust particles from the fuel tank and lines find their way into the bowl along with condensed moisture. The presence of dirt or moisture indicates the possibility of jet plugging and check-valve leakage. It also indicates a faulty fuel filter.

If the float is mounted in the bowl it can be lifted from the bowl with its hinge pin. Be sure to check the positioning of splash baffles and float bounce spring. They must be reinstalled in the same manner during assembly. The float bowl can be thoroughly dried and wiped out. If this does not suffice, the remainder of the carburetor should be removed from the engine and serviced as described in the next section of this chapter.

One of the most common problems that prevents idle mixture adjustment is a plugged idle tube restriction. Plugging usually occurs in the tip end of the small idle tube located in the main well. If the idle tube is located on the discharge cluster the cluster can be removed and all of the passages blown free with compressed air, including all air-bleed passages. The acceleration and main discharge systems can also be blown out but because of their large size they rarely become plugged.

The venturi, discharge nozzle, throttle plates, and carburetor barrel are usually found to be dark

Fig. 7-18 Carburetor jetting in the bowl cover.

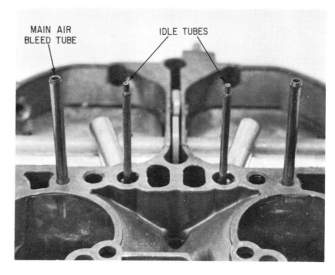

Fig. 7-20 Typical idle tube restriction on the end of the idle tube.

brown or black. This color is the result of the deposits left as the liquid fuel evaporates from the surface. The deposits are a combination of gasoline dyes and carbon that can be removed by coating them with carburetor flushing chemicals sold in small cans at service stations. A clean squirt-type oil-can makes a good dispenser to get the flushing chemical solvents on the deposits within the carburetor bore. Special care should be used to make sure that the solvent thoroughly coats the choke shaft, choke piston, throttle shaft, and idle outlets in the carburetor bore. A small amount of solvent put down the idle passages will loosen any deposits that may have developed in them. The solvent does not have to be cleaned from the surfaces because it will be washed out by the gasoline when the carburetor is reassembled and the engine is started.

While the carburetor is open the acceleration system can be serviced. The pump system can fail from pump-cup rubber or diaphragm deterioration; improperly seating check valves; plugged discharge nozzle; or leaks from the passage at faulty gaskets. New acceleration-pump rubber parts and check valves are included in the carburetor repair kit along with new gaskets. A shop magnet will usually lift the check valves from the carburetor while it is installed on an engine. An alternate method not recommended is to use air pressure to blow the valves from their seats while a shop towel is placed over the carburetor to catch them; they must not fall into the carburetor bore. Air pressure can be blown through the carburetor passages and the discharge nozzle to remove any moisture or loose particles.

Float Level. A new float-needle valve and seat are included in carburetor repair kits and they can be installed during minor carburetor service if they are required. The old seat is removed and the new one is installed using a new seat gasket. The needle valve seat should be firmly tightened using a *properly fitting* wrench or screwdriver, as required.

One of the most important service items to be accomplished during minor carburetor service is to set the float level. Correct float level is necessary for proper fuel metering and engine performance. A number of methods are used for float level measurement. The simplest method is to measure from the top of the bowl surface to a specified place on the float, usually the top or the bottom. Gauges,

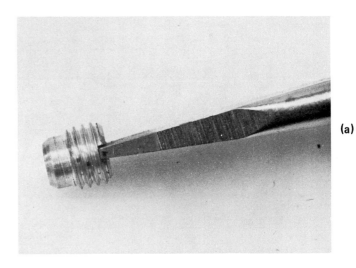

(a)

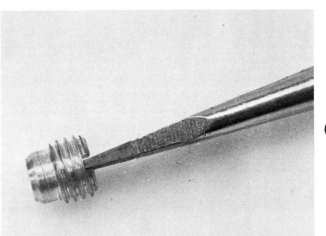

(b)

Fig. 7-21 Screwdriver fit for removing or installing a jet. (a) Correct fit, (b) incorrect fit.

often supplied in the repair kit, are made to the correct dimension and are much faster to use than a measuring scale. Some carburetor float levels are measured with the gasket in place while others are set with the gasket removed.

If the float assembly is mounted in the carburetor bowl cover it can be inverted; this allows the normal weight of the float to hold the needle valve closed while the float level is measured. If the float assembly is mounted in the bowl and it is still on the engine, the float needle will have to be carefully held closed by hand. Pressure on the needle valve will distort the Viton tip of the needle so the resulting float level will be inaccurate.

If the float level is not correct it can be adjusted by bending the float arm tang that touches the needle valve. This should be done carefully so that no other part of the float arm is bent. If the float has two pontoons both of them must be at

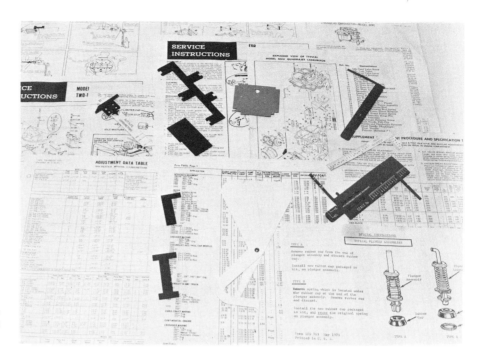

Fig. 7-22 Typical gauges and specifications found in a carburetor repair parts kit.

(a)

(b)

(c)

(d)

Fig. 7-23 Measuring float level adjustment, (a)-(f).

89

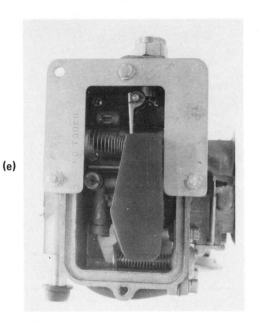

(e)

(f)

the same height before the tang is adjusted. See the appropriate service manual or instruction sheet that comes in the repair kits for specific adjustment details for the carburetor being serviced.

The float assembly is also checked for float drop. This adjustment is to make sure the float needle valve can open fully and it also makes certain that the float does not hit the bottom of the float bowl. Float drop is measured in a fashion similar to float level but it is not quite as critical.

Fuel Level. Float level is used to establish the level of the fuel in the float bowl. When the level of the fuel in the bowl is checked it is called the *wet fuel level*. If the float pontoon has been slightly distorted, such as by a partial collapse of a brass float or fuel absorption of a plastic float, the float level can be set exactly but the wet fuel level will be too high because the pontoon will sink low in the fuel. The wet fuel level can be measured on some carburetors by removing a cap or cover. On

Fig. 7-24 Measuring float drop.

(a)

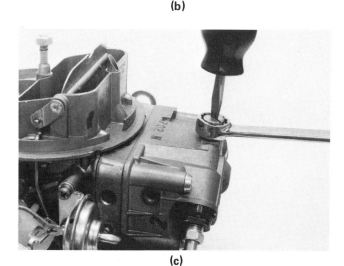

(b)

others it can be measured with the bowl cover removed. Still others have a gauge that can be mounted outside the carburetor to show the wet fuel level. The float level should be adjusted to give the correct wet fuel level for proper engine operation.

Assembly. The bowl cover should be checked with a straightedge to see that it is flat. If the cover is warped it may be possible to work down the high spots by moving the cover across abrasive paper that has been placed on a flat surface. In other cases the possible leakage across a warped cover can be sealed by using a thicker bowl cover gasket or by using two gaskets. Excessively warped covers and bowls should be replaced.

Replacement items used during minor service may consist of a gasket set only. The replacement items could also include the parts that come in a simple carburetor repair kit, which usually contain the gaskets, float-needle valve and seat, acceleration pump, check valves, and assembly clips. Some repair kits include parts that are usable for several different setting numbers on a carburetor type, so some new parts will be left over. Care is required in selecting the correct parts from those supplied in the repair kit. It is best to match them with the old parts for final identification. After the parts are installed and adjustments are made, the bowl cover

Fig. 7-25 Measuring fuel level.

Fig. 7-26 Flattened parting surface of a carburetor bowl.

speed and mixture will have to be readjusted as previously described.

can be installed. It should be lowered straight down over the bowl; the technician should be careful to guide the accelerator pump plunger and metering needles into their proper openings. Be sure that the acceleration pump rubber does not become twisted. Then install and tighten the assembly screws. If the carburetor parts are made of zinc the assembly screws should be carefully torqued. If they are made of aluminum the assembly screws may be tightened as securely as possible with a properly fitting screwdriver. The fuel line, choke linkage or heat tube, and vacuum kick are then reconnected. Where required, adjustments should be made.

If the carburetor is dry a relatively long engine cranking period will be required to fill the carburetor with sufficient gasoline to start the engine. Some technicians put gasoline in the carburetor bowl before trying to start the engine. With the parking brake set and the transmission in neutral the engine is started and warmed up. The wet fuel level may be rechecked on some carburetors when it controls the fuel in its normal operating condition. When the engine is thoroughly warm the idle

7-3 MAJOR CARBURETOR SERVICE

The carburetor is removed from the engine for major carburetor service. To remove the carburetor it is necessary to remove the throttle linkages, choke cross-over link or heat tube, fuel line, and vacuum hoses including the PCV hose in some applications. Carburetors using coolant to heat the choke or carburetor base may need to have some of the engine coolant drained before the coolant attachments on the carburetor are disconnected. Removal of the base flange attaching nuts or cap screws will free the carburetor so it can be lifted from the engine.

For major service, the carburetor is completely disassembled except for the throttle plates, choke plate, air-valve plates, and permanently installed caps and plugs. If these items are faulty the applicable service manual procedures should be followed. The bowl cover, acceleration pump, discharge cluster, and needle valve and seat are removed as described in the previous section of this chapter. In addition, the throttle body is removed from the float bowl body on three-part carburetors. The

Fig. 7-27 Removing a carburetor for overhaul.

Fig. 7-28 Removing a power valve piston from a bowl cover.

vacuum-kick diaphragm assembly is removed along with the anti-dieseling solenoid and all other electrical or rubber parts, such as the bowl vent, air-filter gasket, and limiter caps. Some idle screws are retained with locks that prevent over-rich mixtures so these screws cannot be turned out. Idle mixture screws that turn freely by hand should be removed.

As the carburetor is disassembled the parts should be thoroughly examined to identify any abnormal wear, leakage, or cracks. It is usually advisable to make this inspection before cleaning so that the evidence is not removed from the part. The throttle and choke plate closing should be checked to see if there is any binding or looseness and to see that they fit properly when they are closed. The technician can check throttle plate fit if he holds the plates completely closed, with the idle speed screw loosened, while he sights through them toward a light. Any alignment problems should be corrected before assembly.

Except for the float, all metal parts that can be removed from the carburetor without gaskets or rubber parts attached should be placed in a metal basket and submerged in carburetor chemical cleaner. The technician should avoid getting his hands into the chemical because it removes the natural skin oil and may cause irritation. Carburetor chemical cleaner is available in 5 gallon cans with a basket included. The cleaning time can be reduced by occasionally moving the basket up and down in the cleaner to agitate it. Fresh chemical cleaner will clean carburetor parts in about 5 minutes; used cleaner will take longer. Stubborn deposits may require loosening with a stiff bristle brush.

When the parts are free of deposits they are removed from the chemical cleaner and the excess chemical is poured back into the cleaner can. The basket with parts can then be washed with water, preferably hot water so they will dry more quickly, to remove all of the chemical cleaner. Water is blown from the parts, and holes are blown out with clean compressed air. Make sure all passages and circuits are open. This will remove any loose material and will completely dry the parts. After this type of cleaning the parts should look like new. They should

Fig. 7-29 Parts of a carburetor placed in a basket to be soaked in a cleaning chemical.

Fig. 7-30 Parts removed from the cleaning chemical and washed in hot water before being blown dry with clean compressed air.

be reexamined to determine if any damage is visible that was not apparent before cleaning. Wire should *never* be used to push deposits from carburetor holes or jets. The wire is very likely to damage the jet opening shape, causing it to meter improperly. Carburetor mating surfaces should be checked to see that they fit correctly. If they do not the surfaces should be carefully filed or lapped so that they will fit to prevent leakage.

Two different types of parts kits are available for carburetor service, the one described for minor carburetor service and a complete carburetor overhaul kit. This complete kit contains all of the parts

in the simplified kit plus all new jets and power-system parts. It costs about three times as much as the simplified kit and so it is only used when the carburetor requires all of these new parts.

Often a carburetor does not work as well after service as it did before being serviced. This is the result of incorrect assembly or of assembly with incorrect parts. Parts kits are usually designed to service a number of different carburetor applications so they may include two or more bowl cover gaskets, different assembly clips, and different check valves. The technician must select the correct ones for the carburetor he is working on. In addition there is always the possibility that the wrong parts were placed in the kit or the kit was mismarked with the wrong part number. It is therefore necessary to carefully follow the service procedures in the service manual or the instructions packaged in the parts kit.

The new parts are installed and adjustments are made as described in the previous section on minor carburetor service. The carburetor is assembled dry, without lubricants or sealing compounds, using new gaskets and seals. Screws and plugs are tightened securely with properly fitting wrenches and screwdrivers, unless specific tightening torques are specified. These procedures should be followed to avoid leakage and to provide proper metering. The idle mixture screws should be *carefully* turned clockwise until they bottom, then loosened counterclockwise one and one-half turns for an initial position. The engine will usually keep running with this initial setting. The limiter caps should remain off until idle adjustment has been completed.

The carburetor base gasket is installed on the manifold. The gasket may not be symmetrical so it must be installed correctly to allow vacuum to reach the required carburetor ports. When special positioning is required the gasket is usually marked

Fig. 7-31 Parts laid out on a bench for assembly.

8

Fuel System Service

The automotive fuel system, as discussed in this chapter, consists of the gasoline tank, fuel pump, fuel filter, and connecting lines. Gasoline is stored in the tank that is located under the rear floor pan in front-engine automobiles. Rear-engine automobiles usually mount the fuel tank in front of the passenger compartment. The tank is vented to allow vapors and air to move in and out of the tank in order to keep pressures nearly equal as the vehicle goes up and down hills, as atmospheric pressures change, and as fuel is drawn from the tank. On emission-controlled automobiles the tank is vented through a vapor separator and a carbon canister to keep the gasoline vapors from contaminating the atmosphere. The filler neck of emission-controlled automobiles is fitted with a sealed cap. The cap has a pressure valve and a vacuum valve that allow excessive pressures to equalize. This will prevent damage to the tank if the normal evaporative emission-control vent system fails to operate properly. The filler neck is smaller on automobiles that use no-lead gasoline exclusively.

A diaphragm-type fuel pump, usually mounted on the engine, moves the gasoline from the tank to the engine through a very-fine-grain filter to the carburetor or fuel injection system. Sometimes an electrically driven turbine-type pump is used in the fuel line or in the gasoline tank. To function correctly the pump must deliver· liquid gasoline in sufficient volume and pressure to keep the carbure-

tor bowl full of clean gasoline, regardless of vehicle speed or maneuvering.

When the fuel system malfunctions it is up to the technician to locate and correct the cause. The only thing the automobile operator can do is to have the proper grade of gasoline put into the tank. Three general grades of gasoline are readily available: leaded regular, leaded premium and low-lead or no-lead. All late model engines are designed to run on no-lead gasolines.

8-1 FUEL SYSTEM OPERATION

The fuel pump moves the gasoline in the fuel system. It transfers gasoline from the tank to the carburetor or fuel injection system. Most engine-mounted diaphragm-type fuel pumps are operated by an eccentric lobe on the camshaft. A spring-loaded arm is held against the eccentric lobe, contacting it at all times. In some systems a short push rod is fitted between the eccentric lobe and the spring-loaded arm. The cam-actuated lever arm pulls the diaphragm from the fuel chamber side, increasing its volume and thereby drawing fuel from the gasoline tank. A spring on the lever side of the diaphragm pushes against the diaphragm as the cam eccentric lobe movement relaxes its pull on the arm lever and diaphragm. This spring pressure on the diaphragm is the force that puts pressure on the

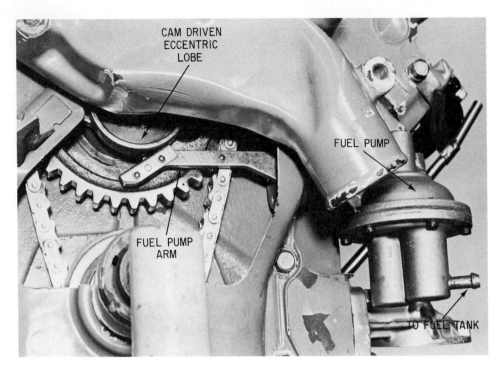

CAM DRIVEN ECCENTRIC LOBE

FUEL PUMP

FUEL PUMP ARM

TO FUEL TANK

Fig. 8-1 Typical fuel pump drive method.

fuel. This force moves the fuel toward the carburetor or fuel injector. The fuel pump is fitted with two check valves, one on the tank side of the pump that will only allow gasoline to go into the pump (inlet check valve) and the other on the engine side of the pump that will only allow gasoline to leave the pump (outlet check valve). As the pump fuel chamber is made to increase in volume by the linkage, gasoline is drawn into the pump from the tank through the inlet check. As the pump fuel chamber is made to decrease in volume by the spring, gasoline is pushed toward the engine through the outlet check.

Connecting fuel lines are made of steel or synthetic rubber hose. Steel tubing uses standard flare-type fittings to connect between the system components and beads to connect to hoses. Synthetic rubber fuel line hoses are fitted snugly over the beads on the ends of the tubing or over nipples at the system components. They are usually secured to the tubing and nipple with a hose clamp. In some cases the hose is fitted with a flare-type metal fitting end. The tubing or hose must be in good condition so that the gasoline does not leak out from or air does not leak into the system on the tank side of the pump during its intake stroke.

The gasoline tank is provided with an elaborate vapor separator that is designed to vent the tank with the automobile standing in any position. It is located within a chamber of the automobile body where it may be difficult or impossible to see

without extensive work. It rarely causes a problem so it is not considered to be a part of normal vehicle service. Details of this system, the vapor separator and the vapor canister, are discussed in Chapter 4 on emission control.

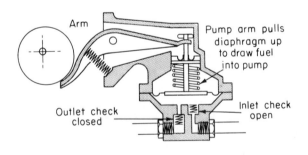

Arm

Pump arm pulls diaphragm up to draw fuel into pump

Outlet check closed

Inlet check open

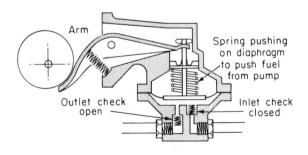

Arm

Spring pushing on diaphragm to push fuel from pump

Outlet check open

Inlet check closed

Fig. 8-2 Section view of a typical diaphragm fuel pump on the inlet and outlet strokes.

102

A most important characteristic of gasoline is that it must be able to start the engine. This sounds extremely fundamental but its importance can best be demonstrated if one tries to start a cold automobile engine on diesel fuel. Fuel must be able to vaporize. This characteristic is called *volatility*. A basic fact that must be remembered is that the fuel must be in the vapor form to burn. It must also be mixed with air in the correct proportions, which is the function of the carburetor or fuel injector. Lastly, the fuel vapors must be intimately mixed with the air. This is accomplished in the intake manifold, head port, and combustion chamber.

All of the gasoline should be consumed in the combustion chamber. If it is not, some of the partially burned fuel can get past the piston rings and into the engine oil. The rest of it will be expelled with the exhaust gases to form unburned hydrocarbon exhaust emissions.

Fuel Filter. Correct carburetor operation requires clean gasoline. A fuel filter is placed in the gasoline supply line to trap any particle that may have been accidently put in the gasoline tank at the service station or any particle that develops within the fuel system of the vehicle.

Periodic fuel filter replacement is recommended by all automobile manufacturers. If their fuel filter replacement recommendation is followed, the operator is unlikely to have a problem from a plugged fuel filter. When the filter becomes plugged, the engine will not produce its usual power or speed. When located outside the carburetor the fuel filter can be checked by running a fuel pump capacity test on the carburetor side of the fuel filter.

Fuel Pump. The fuel pump capacity test is one of the easiest tests to perform, even when a pressure-volume fuel pump tester is not available. The fuel line is disconnected from the carburetor and directed into a measured container. If a shop towel is held around the fitting as it is loosened from the carburetor the towel will absorb any fuel leakage. The saturated towel can be removed from the engine compartment before starting, to reduce the fire hazard that is always present around gasoline. An extension hose is slipped over the fuel line to make it easier to direct the flow of fuel. The engine is started and allowed to idle for 30 seconds as the fuel is being collected in a measured container. The engine is then turned off. Gasoline in the carburetor is sufficient to operate the engine at idle for 30 seconds. The amount of gasoline the fuel pump delivers in one-half minute is measured. The fuel pump specifications give the amount that the fuel pump should deliver in one minute. The amount collected in the 30-second test must be doubled to determine the pump capacity per minute. For example, if 1 pint of fuel were delivered in 30 seconds the fuel pump has the capacity to deliver 2 pints in 1 minute. Fuel pumps will deliver approximately 1 pint per minute on small-displacement engines and approximately 2 pints per minute on large-displacement engines. The appropriate specifications should be checked for any specific engine being tested.

If the fuel system capacity measured on the carburetor side of the fuel filter is normal, no further test is required on the filter. If the capacity is low the test should be repeated on the fuel pump side of the filter. The filter is plugged if the test on the fuel pump side of the fuel filter is normal while the test on the carburetor side is low. If both tests are low, the problem is with the fuel pump operation or with the fuel lines.

In addition to providing volume, the fuel pump is required to produce sufficient pressure to open the carburetor float valve and keep the carburetor bowl full of fuel. Fuel pump pressure is checked by placing a pressure gauge on the outlet side of the fuel pump, usually at the carburetor end of the fuel line, and measuring the fuel pressure as the en-

Fig. 8-3 Running a fuel volume test. A pressure gauge is also included with this specific piece of test equipment.

Fig. 8-4 Making a fuel pump pressure test.

gine idles. Fuel pressures will range from 5 to 10 psi, depending upon the engine. Specific applicable engine specifications should be consulted when making a fuel pressure test. A fuel pump may pass the pressure test but fail the pump capacity test. If the fuel pump eccentric is normal, low fuel pressure indicates that a new pump is needed.

When insufficient fuel volume is produced by the capacity test with gasoline in the tank, a fuel pump vacuum test should be run. To run this test a vacuum gauge is fastened to the tank side of the fuel pump. The fuel lines from the tank will have to be plugged during the test to keep gasoline from leaking out of the line. A normal fuel pump will pull about 10 inches of vacuum (254 mm) at idle. If the vacuum is less, the pump or pump-actuating cam is faulty. A vacuum check at the tank end of the fuel line will indicate air leaks in the line that could cause low fuel-pump volume. A worn pump eccentric or plugged fuel tank filter could cause low pump capacity while still producing the required pressure and vacuum. A broken rocker arm return spring produces a tapping sound but will not affect pump operation.

Air Filter. For the engine to continue to function properly for long periods of time, the air coming into the engine must be clean. Engines are provided with air filters that trap abrasives, dirt, and other contaminants. As the particles are trapped they plug the filter pores. Excessive plugging restricts air flow into the engine and this upsets the carburetor calibration. Air filter plugging produces a fuel rich mixture which in turn reduces engine power and increases carbon monoxide and unburned hydrocarbon exhaust emissions. Badly plugged air filters will limit engine power and speed.

Some manufacturers recommend cleaning the air filter at specific mileage intervals by blowing air from the inside. Others recommend replacing it at set mileages. These schedules should be followed for maximum engine service life. Air filter changes

Fig. 8-5 Air filter replacement.

are required more frequently when unusually dirty operating conditions are encountered. Some equipment companies have developed test methods to indicate air filter plugging. These pieces of test equipment are not commonly used by the automotive service trade.

One of the more accurate air filter checks involves the use of the hydrocarbon-carbon monoxide emission tester. If the engine produces more unburned hydrocarbons and carbon monoxide with the air filter installed than it does with the filter removed, the filter is partly plugged and should be cleaned or preferably replaced.

REVIEW QUESTIONS

1. What part of a diaphragm-type fuel pump puts pressure on the fuel?

2. How will the operator know when the fuel filter becomes plugged?

3. When should the fuel pump vacuum be measured?

4. How can a technician detect an air leak in the fuel line between the tank and fuel pump?

5. How does a dirty air filter affect engine performance?

9

Servicing Emission-Control Devices

The best means of maintaining low emission levels is by giving the engine a good tune-up periodically. On emission-controlled engines the tune-up should include a check of emission-control devices. When these devices are not functioning properly, not only can they produce excessive vehicle emissions but they can affect vehicle drivability and increase fuel consumption. The PCV affects engine idle and crankcase contamination. Ignition timing affects all operations. The air preheat helps to provide drivability during warmup and can cause abnormal combustion after warmup if it continues to provide warm air. Backfiring may result from a malfunctioning air injection system. Rough unstable idle and backfiring can be caused by improper operation of the exhaust gas recirculation system. Evaporative control system problems can affect engine idle and fuel flow from the tank to the fuel pump.

9-1 POSITIVE CRANKCASE VENTILATION

The valve and hoses of the PCV system are simple and easy to service but they are often neglected, just as the exhaust heat riser is neglected. The PCV system allows filtered air to enter the crankcase, usually through the rocker cover. If the PCV inlet filter, located in the air cleaner, is dirty it should be replaced. If a visual inspection of the hoses, both inside and outside, shows deterioration they should be replaced.

The PCV valve is located between the carburetor base and the rocker cover or manifold. The components of the system are interconnected with hoses. The PCV supplies the engine with air at idle. Pinching the hose closed stops the air flow so the engine idle speed will drop about 50 rpm when the PCV is operating normally. If a hydrocarbon tester is available its pickup can be placed at the oil fill cap. It should indicate hydrocarbons when the engine is not running. When the engine is started the hydrocarbon level should immediately drop. The hydrocarbon tester can also be used in its normal tail pipe connection. If the PCV valve is disconnected the hydrocarbon content of the exhaust should decrease.

When the PCV valve does not operate satisfactorily according to one of the above tests it should be serviced. Take-apart PCV valves can be disassembled and cleaned in a carburetor cleaner, but this takes time and labor time is expensive to the customer. New PCV valves are low cost items, and so inoperative PCV valves are usually replaced with new valves. The proper valve should be installed because different engines are designed to operate with different PCV air flows. The valves are manufactured with different plungers and springs even when they may look alike. After a new PCV valve is installed the carburetor idle should be readjusted.

IDENTICAL ENGINES IDLING AT 700 RPM

INITIAL TIMING 8° B.T.D.C.
Relatively little air flow past
carburetor throttle plate which
is in nearly closed position.

INITIAL TIMING 4° B.T.D.C.
Larger throttle plate opening
is needed to allow more air
into the fuel to achieve 700 R.P.M.

Fig. 9-1 Emission controlled engine operates
with the throttle opened more (AC Spark Plug
Division, General Motors Corporation).

9-2 IGNITION TIMING

Basic timing on emission-controlled vehicles is retarded from the *best* timing so it is necessary to
have the throttle open further to provide the same
engine idle speed. This added air allows the engine to
run leaner and along with the higher temperatures
that result from retarded timing helps reduce HC
and CO emission. The amount of exhaust emissions
produced by a given engine is the result of carburetion and the ignition timing effect on combustion.
Basic engine timing must be correct. It is checked
with a timing light while the engine runs at slow

idle with the distributor vacuum hose removed and
temporarily plugged so no air flows into the carburetor. Ignition mechanical centrifugal advance is
based on engine speeds. In engines without emission controls operated at full throttle there is no
vacuum, and so the mechanical centrifugal advance
is the only advance operating. This is also true on
emission-controlled engines, so emission control
modifications of the vacuum advance have *no effect*
on full throttle power produced by the engine. Vacuum advance modified by emission control will
only affect part throttle and idle operation. This
in turn affects fuel economy. Ignition timing con-

Fig. 9-2 Checking engine timing with a timing
light.

trol for low exhaust emission is done by modifying the vacuum applied to the distributor vacuum-advance unit. Distributor vacuum in most vehicles is connected to the carburetor port through a temperature-operated by-pass valve that is also called a thermostatic vacuum switch (TVS), ported vacuum switch (PVS), orifice spark advance control (OSAC), or distributor vacuum control valve. It provides the distributor with normal distributor vacuum from the carburetor vacuum port located just above the throttle plate when the throttle is closed. It

may include an advance delay and this may be temperature compensated. At engine idle the throttle is closed, and so there is no vacuum advance. When the engine overheats during prolonged idle, the thermostatic valve closes the carburetor port and applies full manifold vacuum to the distributor vacuum-control unit to increase combustion efficiency. This fully applies distributor vacuum advance, which increases engine speed thereby lowering the engine temperature. When the engine cools to normal engine temperature the valve returns to its normal position with ported vacuum connected to the distributor advance mechanism.

The thermostatic valve can be checked by applying a test vacuum source to the manifold vacuum port of the valve and increasing the sensor

(a)

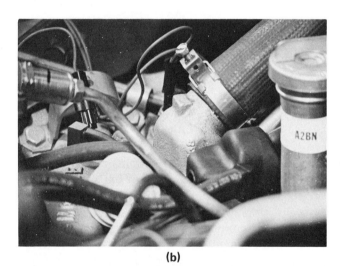

(b)

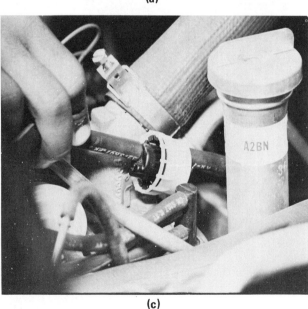

(c)

(d)

(e)

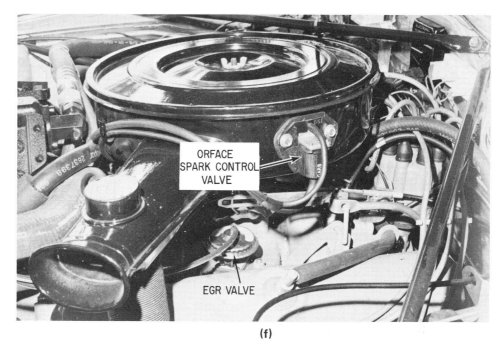

ORFACE SPARK CONTROL VALVE

EGR VALVE

(f)

temperature by heating it with a heat gun such as a hair dryer. A thermometer held next to the sensor will indicate the operating temperature when the port opens to release vacuum.

Many emission-controlled engines use a dual-diaphragm vacuum-advance unit on the distributor. The primary diaphragm is used to advance the ignition timing in the same manner as a single-diaphragm unit. Its vacuum hose is connected to the usual carburetor port just above the closed throttle plate. When the throttle is closed a calibrated spring in the vacuum-advance unit pushes the diaphragm in the ignition retard direction. The secondary diaphragm acts as a stop to limit the amount of retard when no vacuum is being applied to either diaphragm. This is the normal condition for engine starting. As soon as the engine has started, manifold vacuum pulls the secondary diaphragm against a secondary calibrated spring. This action allows the primary calibrated spring to force the primary diaphragm to follow the secondary diaphragm movement, retarding the ignition immediately after starting for minimum emission production. When the throttle is opened a little the engine speed is increased and the carburetor port is exposed to vacuum, which begins to pull the primary diaphragm away from the secondary diaphragm to provide ignition advance that is required for the engine operating conditions. Vacuum advance is fully retarded on deceleration when the throttle is closed and a high manifold vacuum exists. The dual-diaphragm vacuum-advance unit allows normal timing for starting the engine and provides an extended range of ignition timing control while the engine operates.

The operation of the dual-diaphragm vacuum

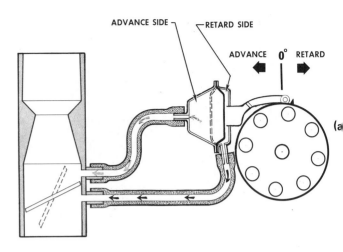

Fig. 9-4 Testing the operating temperature of a ported vacuum switch.

advance unit can be checked by connecting vacuum gauges in the vacuum hoses. It can also be checked by removing the vacuum hoses as the timing mark is being observed with a timing light. Removing the secondary diaphragm hose at idle should produce ignition advance to the basic timing setting with an accompanying increase in engine idle speed. The engine speed is then increased to 2000 rpm with the throttle while the timing mark is still observed with the timing light. Removing the primary vacuum hose should show an ignition retard and slight reduction in engine speed. The operation of the dual-diaphragm can also be checked on a distributor machine by measuring timing change at different vacuum settings compared to the vacuum-advance specifications.

The emission controls that affect ignition vacuum advance during deceleration operate differently on automatic transmission engines than on standard transmission engines. The automatic transmission engine drops rapidly to idle speed when the throttle is closed. Its vacuum advance is quickly and fully retarded to keep the exhaust manifold hot for complete combustion. Standard transmission

Fig. 9-5 Distributor vacuum advance controls that retard at idle and deceleration. (a) Drawing showing principles (AC Spark Plug Division, General Motors Corporation), (b) cutaway distributor.

engines, on the other hand, are driven by the vehicle drive line during deceleration and so the engine cannot slow to idle speed when the throttle is closed. Remember that when the throttle is closed

Fig. 9-6 Deceleration vacuum advance valve with hose connections.

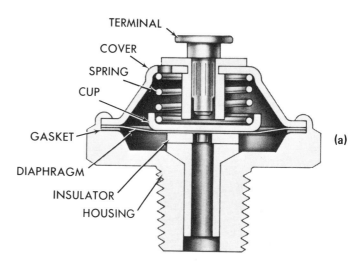

Turbo Hydra-matic 400 TCS Switch (Sectional View)

(a)

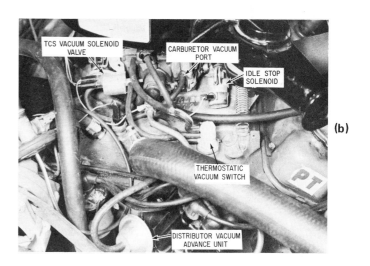

(b)

Fig. 9-7 Transmission controlled spare advance system. (a) Sensor used in an automatic transmission (Chevrolet Motor Division, General Motors Corporation), (b) component parts on an engine.

ported vacuum is zero because the port is above the throttle plate. To provide more time for combustion on these engines the vacuum advance is fully applied by connecting the distributor advance unit to manifold vacuum through the deceleration vacuum-advance valve. The resulting full ignition vacuum advance provides the time required for more complete combustion. When the engine slows to idle speed, normal ported vacuum is again applied to the distributor vacuum unit.

Another approach to the control of emissions is to allow vacuum advance in direct drive only. This is done by putting a switch in the transmission that will control a vacuum solenoid valve in the distributor vacuum-advance hose. The solenoid valve controlling vacuum allows carburetor porting to reach the distributor vacuum unit only when the transmission is in direct drive. In a manual transmission the switch is a mechanically actuated switch and in an automatic transmission it is actuated by direct-drive transmission oil pressure.

When the ignition switch is turned on, the solenoid valve is activated. The solenoid closes the

vacuum hose connecting to the carburetor port and vents the distributor vacuum hose to the atmosphere to prevent any vacuum advance. When the vehicle shifts into direct drive the transmission switch will open the electrical circuit which deactivates the solenoid valve. The deactivated solenoid valve repositions itself to close the vent and connects the distributor vacuum hose to the carburetor vacuum port hose in its normal manner. This system is called a Transmission Controlled Spark (TCS) system by one manufacturer and a Trans-

Fig. 9-8 Testing the operation of a spark delay valve with a vacuum gauge.

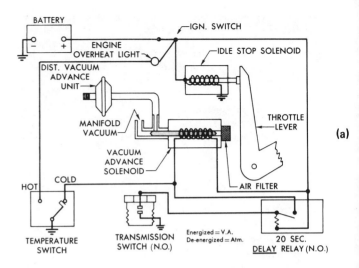

(a)

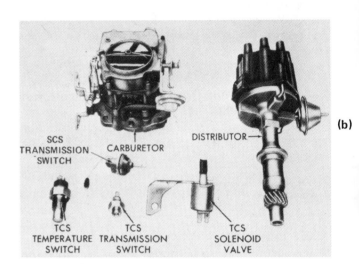

(b)

Fig. 9-9 Transmission controlled vacuum spark advance (AC Spark Plug Division, General Motors Corporation). (a) Schematic of the system, (b) parts used in the system.

mission Regulated Spark (TRS) control system by another manufacturer.

The TCS system can be checked by jacking the drive wheels from the ground and connecting a vacuum gauge in the distributor hose. The vehicle can be started and accelerated through the gears. When it shifts into direct drive with engine speed at 2000 rpm vacuum should be observed on the vacuum gauge. If no vacuum is observed the vacuum hose should be visually checked and the electrical components checked with a test light or voltmeter for opens, shorts, or grounds.

In some vehicle applications the system may also include a temperature switch to advance the ignition when the engine becomes too warm regardless of which drive gear is being used. Both the TCS and TRS systems use the Thermostatic Vacuum Switch (TVS) or Ported Vacuum Switch (PVS) previously described. The TRS system also uses an electrically operated thermal switch that is mounted on the door pillar to sense outside air temperature. It is connected parallel to the transmission switch

so it can by-pass the normal operation of the transmission switch. It remains closed below approximately 55°F (13°C) to hold the electrically operated vacuum spark valve closed to keep the ignition retarded even in direct drive so that the engine will warm up rapidly. Above this temperature the thermal switch opens to allow the transmission switch to control the vacuum solenoid valve. A thermometer and voltmeter are required to check the proper operation of the temperature switch. Cooling will close the switch and warming will open it. It can be cooled by holding ice wrapped in plastic against the switch; and it can be warmed with a light bulb held close to the switch. The voltmeter is used to indicate switch operation and the thermometer adjacent to the switch will indicate the temperature.

Fig. 9-10 Temperature sensors used to modify the distributor vacuum advance and the EGR valve.

Another application uses a speed sensor in place of the transmission switch. It is called an Electronic Spark Control (ESC) system. The speed sensor, consisting either of a rotating magnet and a stationary field winding in a small case, or of fly weights actuating a switch, is connected in series in the speedometer drive cable. As vehicle speed increases the speed sensor voltage-frequency increases or the switch turns on. The voltage frequency signal may need to be fed into a small solid state amplifier in certain applications where the speed sensor electrical output is insufficient. When the speed sensor electrical output is great enough it operates a vacuum-advance electric solenoid valve to connect the distributor vacuum hose to the carburetor port above 23-35 mph (36-56 km), depending on the specific vehicle application. Below this

Fig. 9-11 A cut-away section of a speed control switch used in the speedometer cable.

speed the distributor vacuum hose is vented to atmosphere to prevent ignition vacuum advance. The electronic spark control (ESC) system has approximately the same effect as the transmission regulated spark (TRS) system but it will advance the ignition at the control speed setting even when the transmission is in a gear below direct drive.

The component units of the ESC system are not reparable. If they do not function properly they must be replaced. They can be checked by placing a vacuum gauge in the distributor hose and operating the vehicle with the drive wheels raised. If vacuum is not observed at the proper time the system can be checked using a jumper wire placed around the thermal switch. A voltmeter can be used to check the speed control and amplifier output to determine the speed at which they function. Disconnecting the solenoid wire will break the electrical circuit. The open circuit causes the solenoid to move to a position that will allow ported vacuum from the carburetor to reach the distributor. This will be accompanied by a slight increase in engine speed.

9-3 CARBURETOR CONTROLS

Most emission-controlled automobiles preheat the inlet air to shorten the warmup time when the underhood temperature is below 100°F (38°C). Once the engine is warm the preheat is turned off so that it has no effect on engine operation or performance. Correct operation can be checked visually. One type of preheater is controlled entirely by a thermostat similar to a cooling system thermostat. It is closed when the underhood temperature is below 100°F (38°C). As the engine warms the preheat thermostat gradually opens until it is fully open at 135°F (57°C). The control unit can be checked by placing it in a water bath with a thermometer to indicate the bath temperature. As the bath is heated the temperature at which the preheat thermostat starts to open and becomes fully open can be observed. Some units will also need to have vacuum applied for this test. If the preheat thermostat does not function correctly it will have to be replaced.

Another type of preheat control makes use of a vacuum-diaphragm control, called a vacuum motor, and a temperature-sensing spring. When the engine is cold, before starting, the control damper should be in the cold air position. Immediately

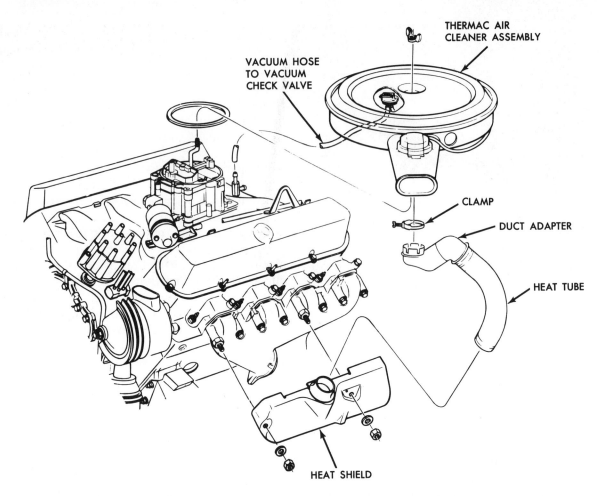

Fig. 9-12 Exploded view of the components in the air preheat system (Cadillac Motor Car Division, General Motors Corporation).

after engine starting, the damper should move to the heat position. As the engine warms the damper will gradually open until it is fully positioned in the cold position when the engine has been warmed to normal temperature. This can be checked by fastening a thermometer in the air cleaner inlet. The damper should be in the cold air position when the temperature is slightly above 100°F (38°C). If the damper does not open, the temperature sensor or vacuum-diaphragm actuator-motor is not operating correctly. The first thing to check is to make sure that the vacuum hoses are in good condition and are installed securely on the proper hose nipples. If they are correctly installed and the damper still does not operate correctly, remove the air cleaner assembly and allow it to cool. Apply a 20 in. (50.8 cm) Hg vacuum source, using either a vacuum pump or a long hose from the manifold vacuum of an idling engine, to the vacuum hose nipple of the heat sensor. This should cause the damper to move to the heat position. If it does not, move the vacuum source directly to the vacuum-diaphragm motor.

If the damper operates, the sensor is not opening at a cool temperature; if it does not operate, the vacuum-diaphragm motor will have to be replaced. Sensor operation can be checked by connecting a vacuum source to the engine hose and a vacuum gauge to the diaphragm hose. Heating and cooling the sensor should cause the sensor to open below 100°F (38°C) and to close at 135°F (57°C).

The carburetor may also be equipped with an anti-dieseling solenoid or an idle-stop solenoid. When the ignition is on the solenoid plunger is out, contacting the throttle idle-stop. It must be in this position when idle speed is adjusted. When the engine is turned off the solenoid is deactivated and the plunger retracts, allowing the throttle plates to completely close so that the engine cannot draw intake air. The solenoid can be checked by placing a jumper wire to connect 12-volt power to the solenoid lead. This should cause the plunger to move out if it is working properly. If the plunger does not move out the solenoid will have to be replaced. If it does not move out when the ignition is on but

Fig. 9-13 Heat sensor for the inlet air preheat.

HEAT SENSOR

Fig. 9-14 Location of an idle-stop solenoid on an engine carburetor.

IDLE-STOP SOLENOID

EGR VALVE

does move out when a jumper is used to power it directly from the battery, there is an open in the electrical feed wire from the ignition switch. This open will have to be located and repaired.

9-4 AIR INJECTION SYSTEM

The air injection system called Thermactor or Air Injection Reactor (AIR) supplies air under pressure to each cylinder exhaust port to help burn combustible products remaining in the exhaust gases. A belt-driven vane-type pump supplies the air. Some of the first pumps were reparable but the modern air injection pump is permanently lubricated and requires no periodic maintenance. It is not to be lubricated in any way, even if it squeaks when turned by hand.

A plastic centrifugal inlet filter-fan is located behind the pump drive pulley. If the engine is to be washed down or steam cleaned the filter should be masked off to keep all cleaning agents out of the

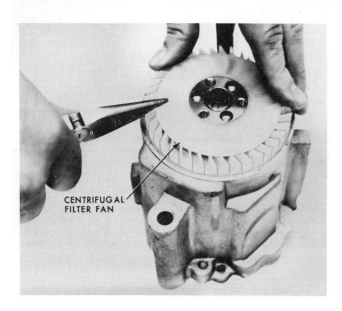

Fig. 9-15 Removing the centrifugal filter-fan from an air pump (AC Spark Plug Division, General Motors Corporation).

pump. The centrifugal filter-fan is the only part of the pump to be serviced. The pulley is removed, then the plastic filter-fan is taken off with a pliers. The filter-fan will usually break up as it is being re-

moved so care must be exercised to keep any plastic chips from entering the pump inlet. It is a recommended precaution to wear safety glasses to prevent particles from getting into the eyes as the plastic breaks. A new filter-fan is installed by drawing it into position with the pulley cap screws.

The air pump must have its belt adjusted correctly to operate properly. Air pump operation can be determined by removing the hose feeding air to the exhaust and feeling the pump outlet air flow. In some cases the outlet is restricted by an 11/32 in. (36 mm) hole in the plug when checking pump operation. This should allow the pump to develop pressure as specified. It is normal for the pump to make some noise that becomes louder as engine speed increases. Air leaks in the system can be felt by hand or they can be checked by brushing soapy water on the hoses, tubing, and connections.

The check valves can be inspected by removing the air hoses. The operation of the valves can be observed by depressing the check with a probe. It should return freely to its original position.

The by-pass or diverter valve operation can be checked by listening at its silencer. One end of a piece of hose held close to the silencer and the other held close to the ear will help the technician to listen to its operation. Engine speed is brought up to 2000 rpm until the speed stabilizes. The throttle is allowed to close suddenly. This closing should be accompanied by a rush of air out of the silencer if the valve is operating correctly. If no rush of air is

Fig. 9-16 Exploded view of the components used in the air injection system (Cadillac Motor Car Division, General Motors Corporation).

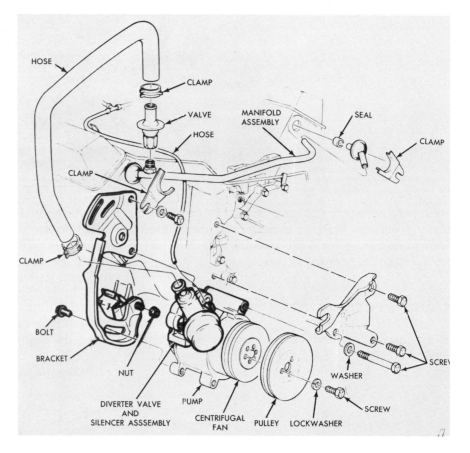

heard or if an exhaust backfire occurs, the by-pass or diverter valve is faulty and must be replaced. The valve is also faulty if air escapes from the silencer at any other time.

After the air injection reactor system is checked the hoses and tubing should be reconnected and left in good condition. All fittings and connections should be tight and the drive belt tension should be adjusted correctly.

9-5 EXHAUST GAS RECIRCULATION

Oxides of nitrogen are controlled with a special camshaft that has a long valve overlap and with a system to return a portion of the exhaust gas back to the combustion chamber. This is called the Exhaust Gas Recirculation (EGR) system. In some Chrysler engines special sized openings are placed in the intake manifold floor below the carburetor to interconnect the heat cross-over passage with the intake passage. Flow is proportional to the difference between intake manifold vacuum and exhaust back pressure. Maintenance of this system requires the removal of the carburetor and an inspection of the orifices each 12,000 miles (19,320 km).

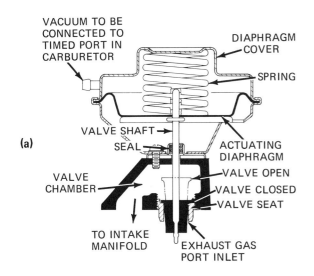

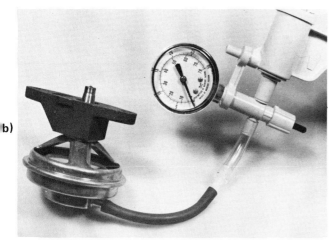

(c)

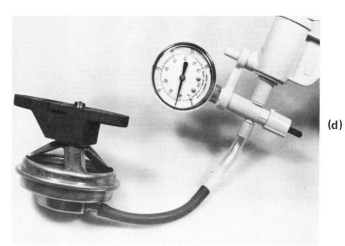

(d)

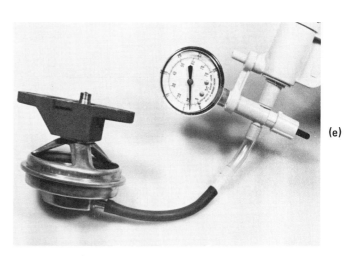

(e)

Fig. 9-17 Details of the EGR valve. (a) Drawing of an EGR valve (Buick Motor Division, General Motors Corporation), (b, c, d, e) EGR valve movement with different amounts of vacuum applied.

117

The most common design uses a vacuum-controlled valve to allow exhaust gases to enter the intake. A spring-loaded diaphragm holds the valve closed. The vacuum chamber located above the diaphragm is connected to a special signal port in the carburetor that connects to a hole or a vertical slot in the carburetor bore or to a port that senses venturi vacuum. As the carburetor throttle plate is opened in the slot-type, it gradually exposes more of the vertical port slot to vacuum. In some applications the vacuum is modified by exhaust pressure. The EGR valve stays closed at idle and at fast idle speeds. It gradually opens as engine speeds are increased. At full throttle it again closes. The actual flow of gases is dependent upon the EGR valve opening position and upon the pressure difference between the gases in the exhaust manifold and the vacuum in the intake manifold. A vacuum amplifier is required to increase the carburetor venturi vacuum port signal.

The operation of this system can be checked by installing a vacuum gauge in the EGR control vacuum hose. The start of EGR may be delayed with a timer. Increasing engine speed should increase vacuum. If it does not, the carburetor passage will have to be examined. The operation of the valve can be checked by removing it from the engine and applying vacuum to the vacuum connection. The valve should begin to move at approximately 3 in. (7.5 cm) Hg of vacuum and be fully open at approximately 8 in. (20.2 cm) Hg of vacuum. If the valve does not function correctly it will have to be cleaned or replaced.

The exhaust gas recirculating controls require the use of a temperature switch in the coolant system. The EGR is inactive at low coolant temperatures. As the coolant warms, the EGR system is activated.

9-6 THERMAL REACTOR AND CATALYTIC CONVERTER

Severe emission standards are not met entirely by engine modifications, and so devices have been developed to finish cleaning the exhaust after it leaves the engine.

A thermal reactor is an insulated exhaust manifold of special design to hold the exhaust temperature at a high level until combustion reactions have had time to be completed. In most applications air is injected into the exhaust to provide more oxygen for combustion. The air is also directed around the metal of the reactor to keep it cooler, thereby increasing the useful life of the reactor. In time the thermal reactor metal burns out. When this occurs the reactor requires replacement just like any other part of the exhaust system.

(a)

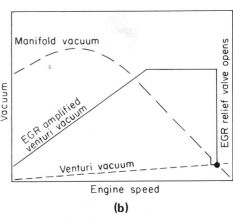

(b)

Fig. 9-18 Vacuum amplifier. (a) Disassembled parts with an assembled vacuum amplifier on the right, (b) graph showing the amplification of vacuum compared to ported and manifold vacuum.

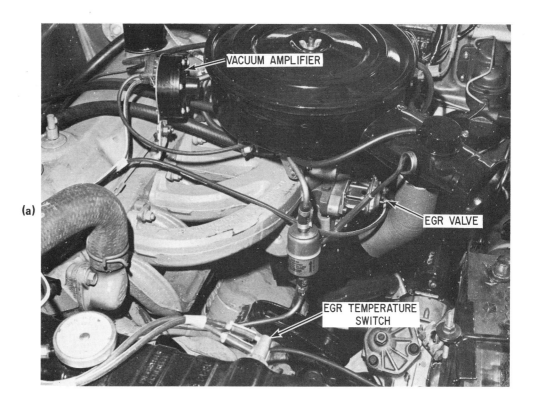

(a)

VACUUM AMPLIFIER

EGR VALVE

EGR TEMPERATURE SWITCH

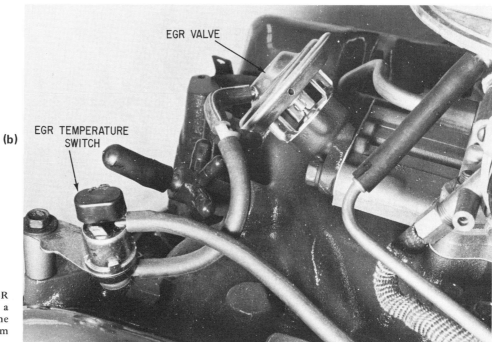

(b)

EGR VALVE

EGR TEMPERATURE SWITCH

Fig. 9-19 Components in an EGR system. (a) On an engine with a vacuum amplifier, (b) on an engine that doesn't require a vacuum amplifier.

Catalytic converters are located in the exhaust pipe between the exhaust manifold and the muffler. They consist of a chamber with a catalyst through which the exhaust gases pass. The catalyst increases the rate of oxidation of the HC and CO in the exhaust and in some cases increases the rate of reduction of NO_x at lower temperatures.

Two things can happen to the catalytic converter. Its case or housing can burn through, allowing the exhaust gas to escape, or the catalyst can become ineffective. This will happen when a cylinder misfires. Ineffective catalyst can be determined with a HC-CO tester. In either case the catalyst or converter will have to be replaced.

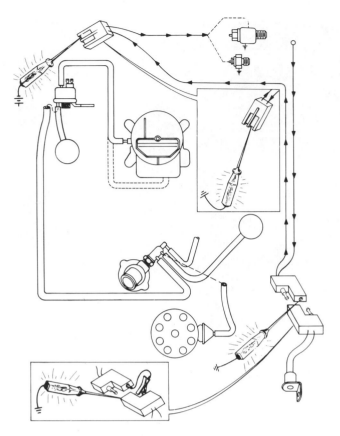

Fig. 9-20 Method of testing electrical emission controls with a test light (American Motors Corporation).

Automobiles equipped with catalytic converters must use only lead-free gasoline. Lead from the gasoline will contaminate the catalyst and make it ineffective. If this happens the catalytic converter will need to be replaced to reduce emissions to the required emission standards. Fuel tank fill necks are designed so that only lead-free gasoline can be used.

9-7 EVAPORATIVE CONTROL SYSTEM

The evaporative control system requires very little service. Its hoses and lines should be secure and in good condition. If they are replaced they must be replaced with special fuel-resistant materials marked EVAP or FUEL. Vapor leaks can best be checked with a hydrocarbon test instrument. The tester pickup should be moved along below the lines. Hydrocarbon vapors tend to sink in air. Observed hydrocarbon readings indicate vapor leaks. The source must be found and repaired.

The gasoline tank filler cap used on emission-controlled vehicles is a pressure-vacuum cap. If it is replaced it must be replaced with the correct type of cap to prevent excess pressure or vacuum that could damage the fuel system parts.

The carbon canister is fitted with a filter. Under normal driving conditions the canister filter should be replaced once each year or each 12,000 miles (19,320 km), whichever comes first. When it is operated under dirty conditions the canister filter should be replaced more often, just as is required of the engine filters. If the filter is changed at proper intervals the activated carbon does not require replacement.

Other parts of the fuel system are not reparable but must be replaced if damaged, worn, or aged to the point that they are no longer effective.

Fig. 9-21 Replacing the filter on the bottom of a carbon canister.

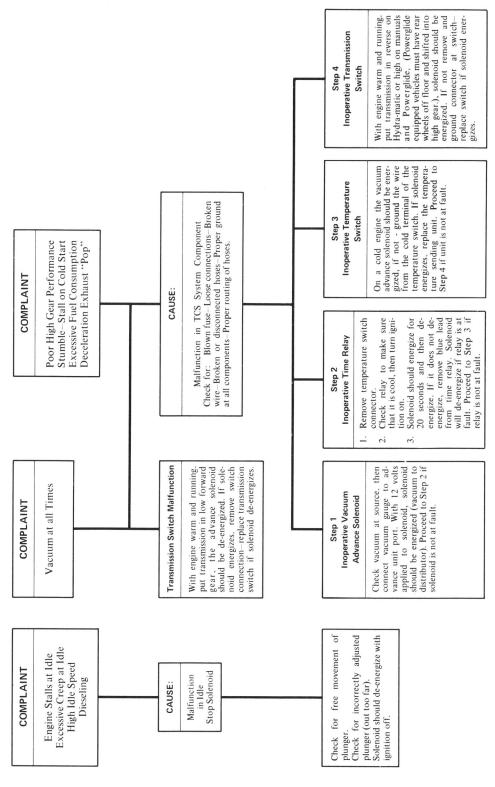

COMPLAINT

Engine Stalls at Idle
Excessive Creep at Idle
High Idle Speed
Dieseling

CAUSE:

Malfunction in Idle Stop Solenoid

Check for free movement of plunger.
Check for incorrectly adjusted plunger (out too far).
Solenoid should de-energize with ignition off.

COMPLAINT

Vacuum at all Times

Transmission Switch Malfunction

With engine warm and running, put transmission in low forward gear, the advance solenoid should be de-energized. If solenoid energizes, remove switch connection—replace transmission switch if solenoid de-energizes.

COMPLAINT

Poor High Gear Performance
Stumble—Stall on Cold Start
Excessive Fuel Consumption
Deceleration Exhaust "Pop"

CAUSE:

Malfunction in TCS System Component
Check for: Blown fuse—Loose connections—Broken wire—Broken or disconnected hoses—Proper ground at all components—Proper routing of hoses.

Step 1
Inoperative Vacuum Advance Solenoid

Check vacuum at source, then connect vacuum gauge to advance unit port. With 12 volts applied to solenoid, solenoid should be energized (vacuum to distributor). Proceed to Step 2 if solenoid is not at fault.

Step 2
Inoperative Time Relay

1. Remove temperature switch connector.
2. Check relay to make sure that it is cool, then turn ignition on.
3. Solenoid should energize for 20 seconds and then de-energize. If it does not de-energize, remove blue lead from time relay. Solenoid will de-energize if relay is at fault. Proceed to Step 3 if relay is not at fault.

Step 3
Inoperative Temperature Switch

On a cold engine the vacuum advance solenoid should be energized, if not - ground the wire from the cold terminal of the temperature switch. If solenoid energizes, replace the temperature sending unit. Proceed to Step 4 if unit is not at fault.

Step 4
Inoperative Transmission Switch

With engine warm and running, put transmission in reverse on Hydra-matic or high on manuals and Powerglide. (Powerglide equipped vehicles must have rear wheels off floor and shifted into high gear), solenoid should be energized. If not remove and ground connector at switch—replace switch if solenoid energizes.

Fig. 9-22. Trouble shooting flow chart for emission controls (Chevrolet Motor Division, General Motors Corporation).

REVIEW QUESTIONS

1. What is the best means of maintaining low emission levels?

2. What emission-control device affects both idle and crank-case contaminants?

3. What emission-control device affects all engine operation?

4. What methods can be used to check the PCV system operation?

5. How does the vacuum advance affect maximum engine power on emission-controlled engines?

6. How is the engine kept from overheating during prolonged idling with retarded ignition?

7. How can vacuum valves or controls be checked?

8. What visual checks should be made when emission-control system problems are suspected?

9. Describe the procedure used to test the intake air preheat.

10. Describe the procedure used to test the air injection system.

Engine
Mechanical Checks

Only three things are needed for an engine to run: compression, fuel, and ignition occurring at the right time in the cycle. This is basic and must be the underlying consideration for all engine trouble shooting problems. Proper engine operation goes a step further; the engine must have sufficient compression and must have the correct air/fuel mixture charge continually being delivered to the combustion chambers. A tune-up essentially involves preventive maintenance operations, exact carburetor adjustments, and correct ignition timing for all operating conditions.

Compression is developed as the piston squeezes the charge on the compression stroke of the engine cycle. The amount of compression pressure developed in the combustion chamber depends upon a full intake charge and minimum leakage as the charge is compressed. The intake and exhaust valve timing must be correct in relation to the engine cycle in order to pull a full charge into the cylinder. The valves are required to seal tightly, the piston rings must seal the small space between the pistons and the cylinder wall, and gaskets must be tight to prevent leakage during compression.

The engine needs fuel to start. Most readers who have had some experience with trying to start a balky engine have poured a small quantity of raw gasoline down the carburetor barrel. The vapors from the gasoline mix with the incoming air to produce a combustible mixture, even if there is no fuel in the carburetor. The function of the carburetor is to supply the correct air/fuel mixture for continued running after the engine first starts.

Ignition is more critical than either compression or carburetion for engine starting. The ignition must be intense enough to jump the spark plug gap and it must occur in the engine cycle just as the piston approaches top center on the *compression* stroke. This allows the charge to push the piston down as it burns and builds up pressure. Ignition timing has to be changed for efficient engine operation and to maintain low exhaust emissions as the engine speed changes and as the engine produces power to move the vehicle.

10-1 TUNE-UP REQUIREMENTS

The routine minor tune-up is usually done to restore engine economy and performance after a number of miles of operation. A minor tune-up can be done using common hand tools and a limited amount of test equipment. The minor tune-up is the type of tune-up usually done by service stations and by individuals who maintain their own automobiles. When a minor tune-up does not correct a problem, more extensive use of test equipment will be required to pinpoint the cause of a problem. Most problems can be found during a major tune-up or by specialized tests made on the specific system that is malfunctioning.

An engine tune-up is a procedure performed

on an engine to make it develop its best perform-ance while it produces the lowest emissions pos-sible. It is usually run at periodic intervals when engine performance has deteriorated, or when the operator wants to be sure that he will have depend-able service on a trip or in winter weather. A tune-up may also be run as a trouble shooting sequence when there is some abnormal engine condition.

The minor tune-up consists of a visual inspec-tion, routine mechanical service, and instrument tests. The visual inspection includes checking the engine mounting and attachments for abnormal conditions, such as checking the condition of all wires, hoses, belts, and carburetor linkages. The engine should be examined for coolant, fuel, oil, and exhaust leaks. Any defects that could affect engine operation or vehicle safety should be re-paired. This might include mechanical service such as retorquing bolts and adjusting belts. Mechanical service also includes servicing the spark plugs and ignition points. It usually includes cleaning or re-placing air and fuel filters and making sure that the vehicle has an adequate supply of oil, coolant, and brake fluid. Instrument checks include engine basic timing, operation of timing advance mechan-isms, and setting engine idle. The minor tune-up might also include the cylinder balance test and a check of the emission-control component operation.

10-2 MECHANICAL CHECKS

A tune-up starts with mechanical checks. Mechan-ical checks include a good visual inspection of the engine and its mounting, attachments, and systems. Leaks should be repaired by installing new gaskets, oil seals, hoses, and tubing or by tightening cover hold-down bolts, cap screws, hose clamps, or tubing fittings. All electrical wires, ignition cables, and vacuum hoses should be in good condition and be properly supported, and should have their termi-nals secure. Engine belts should show no sign of cracks or wear and should be adjusted correctly using a belt tension gauge or torque wrench when the engine components permit. The engine carbu-retor and transmission controls should be checked to see that they are properly mounted and that they function correctly without binding.

Mechanical service usually includes an inspec-tion of the fuel filter, air filter, and PCV valve. These may be routinely replaced during a tune-up

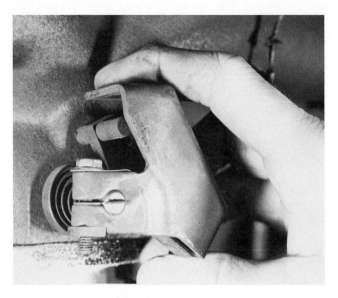

Fig. 10-1 Heat riser valve in the manifold.

as good preventive maintenance procedures to mini-mize engine problems that would inconvenience the customer if his engine were to fail on the road. Inline fuel filters that are in common use are not serviceable so they must be replaced when a new filter is required. Some PCV valves can be disas-sembled and washed in solvents, but others must be replaced. Some air filters may be cleaned. Dirt can be blown from paper filters, from the inside outward, with a low-pressure air gun. However, replacement is more satisfactory. Some plastic foam air filters can be washed in solvents and reused.

The exhaust system heat riser valve should be checked for free operation. Vacuum-operated heat control valves should be checked with vacuum. If stuck they should be serviced. Special solvents can be put on the valve bushings when they are cold. If the solvent does not free the valve a part of the exhaust system will have to be removed for valve service. Vacuum motors are replaceable.

In the service station tune-up, the serviceman will usually replace the spark plugs, possibly take a compression test, install ignition points and con-denser, set the basic ignition timing, and adjust the engine idle speed. Procedures that are used to do these operations are discussed in the following paragraphs.

10-3 SPARK PLUG SERVICE

The spark plug is the end point in the ignition sys-tem. It is located in the combustion chamber where it is subjected to combustion deposits, erosion, and corrosion. Spark plugs require periodic service regardless of the type of ignition system used.

Spark plugs are removed by first removing the spark plug cable. This is done by carefully twisting and pulling the boot that fits over the spark plug to remove it without damaging or stretching the cable. Blow air around the spark plug to remove any loose material. Use a good spark plug socket, with an internal cushion, to remove the spark plug without damage. Generally the spark plugs are removed and laid out in order for inspection. A better practice to follow when a compression test is to be run while the spark plugs are out of the engine is to loosen the spark plugs about one-quarter turn, then start the engine and speed it up two or three times. Any carbon chips that have broken loose from the combustion chamber surface as the spark plugs are turned will be blown from the engine and so they will not get under a valve and cause erroneous compression test readings.

When the spark plugs are removed they should be examined critically. This examination is often called *reading the plugs*. The condition of the electrodes and the type of carbon on the spark plug

nose gives a good indication of how that particular cylinder has been operating.

The most obvious spark plug condition is the type of carbon on the spark plug nose. Normal spark plugs will have a light tan to gray deposit, depending on the additives in the gasoline that has been used. If the deposits are slight and white with badly eroded electrodes, the cylinder has been running very hot. Heavy sooty deposits indicate rich air/fuel mixtures and heavy wet deposits indicate high oil consumption. Some engines, especially ones with high mileage, tend to develop a heavy white deposit that bridges the gap. This is a result of oil consumption that forms the deposits. Spark plug manufacturers supply full-color pictures of these conditions so that the technician can compare the spark plug appearance and diagnose the problem.

Spark plugs can be cleaned and serviced; however it is the general practice to install new spark plugs on a tune-up being done on a customer's engine. The customer is confident the engine will get another 10,000 miles or more before the next tune-up and so he assumes new spark plugs will be installed.

Cleaning is the first step when spark plugs are to be serviced. Spark plug cleaners are available to sand blast the electrode end of the spark plug to remove carbon deposits. Excessive sand blasting should be avoided because it will erode the spark plug insulator nose and the electrodes. The spark plug threads should be cleaned with a wire brush, and the top insulator and terminal should be wiped clean. The spark plug can then be given a good visual inspection to see that the insulator shows no signs of cracking and that the electrodes are not excessively burned. The gap of each serviceable spark plug is somewhat enlarged so a point file can be inserted between the electrodes to file the center electrode flat. This reduces the voltage required to fire the spark plug. The gap is reset to specifications and the spark plugs are ready to be installed. It is considered a good practice to use a wire gauge for measuring spark plug gaps.

Spark plugs are manufactured in a number of heat ranges. The heat range is part of the spark plug numbering code. It is always advisable to reinstall spark plugs with the same heat range when the spark plug nose appears normal. If the removed spark plug appears burned, a colder heat range spark

Fig. 10-2 Typical spark plug conditions (The Prestolite Company).

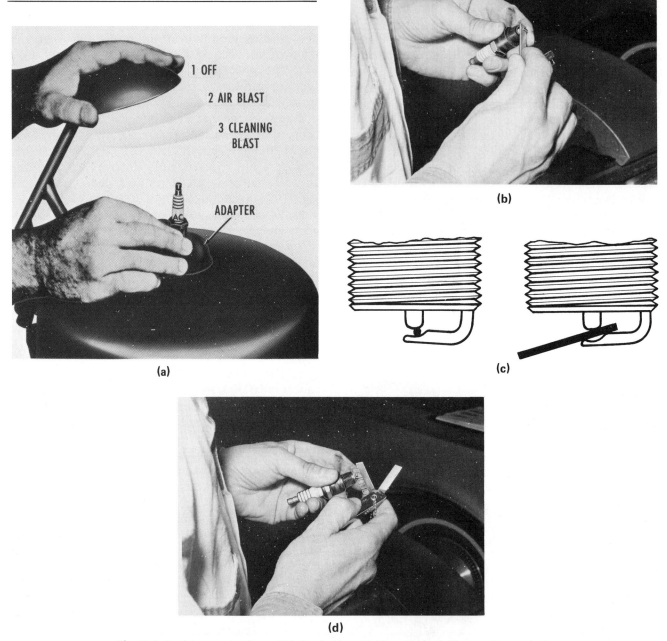

Fig. 10-3 Servicing spark plugs (AC Spark Plug Division, General Motors Corporation). (a) Cleaning, (b) filing the gap, (c) gap measurement, (d) gap adjustment.

plug can be installed and if the removed spark plugs have heavy carbon deposits, a hotter-range spark plug can be used. The engine manufacturer's recommendation should be followed. If excessively high heat range spark plugs are inadvertently installed in an engine they will run so hot that they will cause preignition, which will damage the pistons and may damage the valves. Spark plugs that are too cold will foul and misfire, producing unburned hydrocarbon emissions.

It is a recommended procedure to run a spark plug tap through the spark plug hole to clean the threads before reinstalling the spark plugs, although this is seldom done. The electrode gap of all new spark plugs should be checked and adjusted to specification before they are installed to correct any gap change caused by careless handling. Where spark plug gaskets are used, new gaskets are generally recommended for use on both new and used spark plugs to give the proper seating contact that

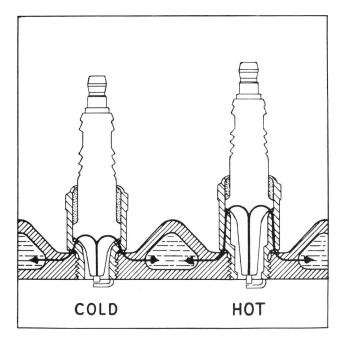

Fig. 10-4 The cooling path of the spark plug that controls
its heat range (Champion Spark Plug Company).

helps transfer nearly half of the heat from the spark
plug to the head. Spark plug manufacturers recommend correct spark plug tightening torque to provide maximum service life. The recommended
torque is achieved by turning the spark plug about
one-half turn past finger-tight when a *new* gasket
is used. Tapered-seat spark plugs should be seated
firmly enough to assure a gas-tight seal. Spark plug
cable clips should be firmly seated on the spark plug
and cables should be properly supported in clips
provided. In some cases the cables are purposely
crossed to eliminate cross-firing caused by induction between the secondary cables.

When new secondary cables are required it is
critical for maximum service to get cables that will
withstand the high underhood temperatures of emission-controlled engines. Some engines require expensive silicone insulation on the cables to meet
high-temperature requirements. It is the responsi-
bility of the technician to install the correct type
of secondary cable. All modern engines use resist-
ance-type secondary cables to minimize radio and
television interference.

10-4 ENGINE CONDITION

The engine must be in good mechanical condition
in order for the fuel and electrical systems to do
their jobs properly. The ability to develop high
equal compression in each cylinder is the key mech-

anical factor in engine tune-up. It is usually checked
on a warmed-up engine at the same time as spark
plugs are serviced.

The deposits on the spark plugs give an indication of how each cylinder has been running. A
compression test will provide additional information about the engine. During the compression test
the engine is usually cranked with a remote starter
switch so all the work can be done under the hood.
Procedures shown in the service manual will have
to be followed in automobiles using a seat belt-
starter interlock.

Compression of each cylinder is measured by
cranking the engine with a compression gauge connected in the spark plug hole. With the throttle
fully open the engine is cranked through exactly
five compressions. The gauge reading should rise
to nearly full pressure as the piston comes up on
the first compression stroke. Cylinder compression
pressure shown on the gauge after the fifth compression stroke should be recorded as compression
pressure. Gauge pressure is then released, the gauge
pick-up moved to the next cylinder, and the sequence repeated. This is done on each of the engine cylinders. The gauge readings obtained can be
checked against specifications to determine if they
are up to standard. Engines with compression
ratios of 8.0:1 to 8.5:1 have minimum compression
pressures as low as 100 psi (6894.75 Pa). The 8.5:1
to 9.5:1 compression ratio engines have minimum
pressures of 125 psi (8618.46 Pa). Engines with
compression ratios in the 9.5:1 to 10.5:1 range
have minimum compression pressures of 140 psi
(9652.65 Pa). Normal compression pressures are
30 to 40 psi (2068.4 to 2757.9 Pa) higher than the
minimum allowable pressures. A smooth running
engine depends upon equal compression pressures
between cylinders. If the lowest cylinder pressure
is at least 70% of the highest, the engine will be able
to run smoothly. Some manufacturers allow a 20
psi (1378.9 Pa) variation and some allow a variation
as high as 40 psi (2757.9 Pa) between cylinders
considered to have normal compression.

Low compression pressure does not indicate
the specific cause of the low pressure. One way to
help pinpoint the problem is to follow the compression test with a *wet compression check*. About a
tablespoon (15 ml) of motor oil is put into each
cylinder through the spark plug hole and the engine cranked a few revolutions to help the oil flow
around the piston rings, sealing them. The com-

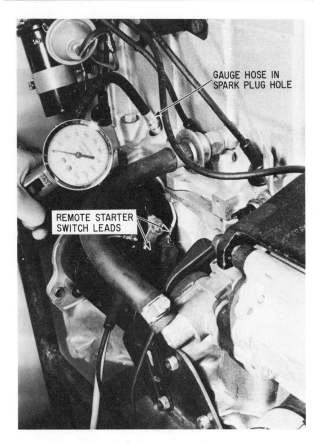

Fig. 10-5 Using a compression gauge.

pression test sequence is rerun with the cylinders wet with oil. If the pressures greatly increase over the low compression pressures of the dry test, the low pressures are due to piston ring leakage. If the wet test shows only slight increases in pressure the low pressure problem is due to valve leakage. If two adjacent cylinders have low compression, both dry and wet, it may be due to head gasket failure allowing compression to leak between them. Low compression may be the result of a temporary deposit build-up on the valves caused by low-speed city driving. Repeated hard accelerations in freeway driving will remove this type of deposit. If a compression retest shows the same low readings the engine will have to be repaired before a tune-up will satisfactorily improve performance. In any case the cylinder head will have to be removed to repair the problem before any other tune-up procedure will be able to help the engine run properly. If compression is normal the spark plugs can be serviced and the engine tune-up can be completed.

Sometimes it is difficult to pinpoint the cause of low compression. A *cylinder leakage* test that puts air into a cylinder at a measured rate is useful in pinpointing the cause of low compression. Excessive leakage is indicated by a high leakage reading on the gauge. In reality this is a low pressure reading because the air leaks out as fast as it is put in. If air leaks from the tail pipe an exhaust valve is leaking. If air can be heard leaking from the carburetor an intake valve is leaking. If air can be heard leaking from the oil filler cap the rings are leaking. During this test the rings are not moving as they normally do in a running engine so some ring leakage is normal. Leakage into the cooling system will show up as bubbles in the coolant that can be seen when the filler cap is removed and the coolant filled up into the filler neck.

The cylinder leakage test is run on a warmed-up engine by cranking the engine to bring one piston to top center. A hose is attached between the cylinder leakage instrument and an adapter screwed into the spark plug hole. The instrument is calibrated by adjusting the air pressure to 0% leakage

Fig. 10-6 A tester used to measure cylinder leakage.

with the hose blocked. It is connected to the adapter to allow air to flow into the cylinder. If the cylinder did not leak the pressure in the cylinder would also go to a 0% leakage reading. With normal leakage past the rings the cylinder will show 20% or less leakage. A problem is indicated if a cylinder has more than 20% leakage.

After the top center of one cylinder is found, a timing wheel can be attached to the distributor rotor to be used to help bring each piston to top center so that a cylinder leakage test can be run on it. The test sequence is run on each cylinder following the cylinder firing order.

An engine in good mechanical condition will run with high manifold vacuum. Manifold vacuum is developed as the pistons move down on the intake stroke to draw the charge from the carburetor and manifold. Air to replenish the manifold comes past the throttle plate into the manifold. Vacuum will increase any time the engine turns faster or has better cylinder sealing while the throttle plate remains in a fixed position. Manifold vacuum will decrease when the engine turns more slowly or when the cylinders do an inefficient job of pumping.

A test of *manifold cranking vacuum* is a good supplementary test to help measure the mechanical condition of the engine. Cranking vacuum is not affected by carburetion or ignition. The throttle plate is adjusted so that it closes completely. Remember to keep track of the number of turns made on the idle speed adjusting screw so that the idle speed can be repositioned in its original position

when this test is completed. The engine is cranked with a vacuum gauge attached to a manifold port and cranking vacuum is noted. No specifications are used. A relatively high even vacuum indicates normal mechanical condition. Unsteady vacuum indicates a cylinder with low compression caused by a leaking valve or by leaking piston rings. An even, low reading indicates that the entire engine is in poor mechanical condition.

Another test of engine performance can be done without special equipment on engines that do not use a catalytic converter. While watching the engine speed change on a tachometer connected to a running engine, remove a spark plug cable from one spark plug at a time. Insulated pliers are useful to remove the ignition cables to avoid getting an electric shock. The engine speed should drop an equal amount as each cable is removed. If the rpm drop when one ignition cable is removed is less than the drop when a cable is removed from one of the other cylinders, the cylinder with the least drop has not been producing its share of the engine power. The cylinder with the least drop has some malfunctioning component. Many brands of test equipment have a built-in electronic circuit that can short out one or more cylinders at a time merely by positioning a switch, without removing the ignition

Firing order 18436572

First half	1	8	4	3
Second half	6	5	7	2
	First pair	Second pair	Third pair	Fourth pair

(a)

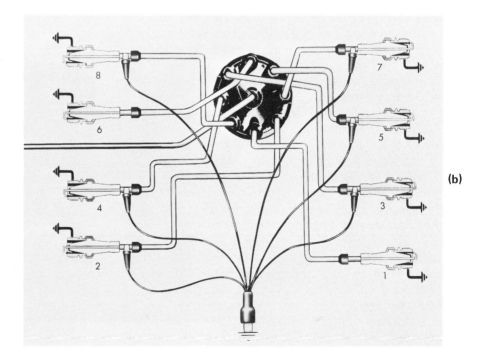

(b)

Fig. 10-7 Cylinder balance. (a) Calculating the balance pairs, (b) hook-up procedure to run cylinder pairs 1 and 6 (Chevrolet Motor Division, General Motors Corporation).

cables. An expanded-scale tachometer is used to magnify the reading so that the technician can easily and quickly see small changes in the engine-speed drop. If this test were performed on an engine with a catalytic converter the fuel from the nonfiring cylinder would ignite in the converter. This would produce excessive temperatures that would ruin the catalyst.

The principle of operating the engine on part of the cylinders, with the other cylinders dragging to provide a load because they are not firing, can be illustrated with an old but simple test called a *cylinder balance test*, using only a set of jumper leads and a set of extenders to provide an exposed conductor between the spark plug rubber boot and the spark plug terminal. It is not normally done at this time in a tune-up sequence, but it is mentioned here because it is another means of measuring the engine mechanical condition. It must not be used on engines with catalytic converters. In this test some of the cylinders are shorted out to prevent ignition so that they will be driven by the remaining operating cylinders. This emphasizes the weak cylinder by causing it to drive more than one non-firing cylinder. Before the test is started, the shorting sequence must be determined to maintain even firing pulses. The first half of the firing order is written above the second half as shown in the accompanying illustration (Figure 10-7). Cylinders are paired using the cylinders numbered one above the other. With a tachometer and vacuum gauge attached, the engine is run at approximately 1500 rpm with all the cylinders firing. The cylinders not in the operating pair being checked are shorted out with jumper wires. This allows the engine to operate on one pair of cylinders. Vacuum and speed are noted. Shorting wires are moved to allow another pair of cylinders to operate and vacuum and speed are again noted. This procedure is continued until all pairs have been run. The pair developing the lowest vacuum and speed are doing the least work. The specific cylinder at fault can be identified by shorting out every other cylinder in the firing order. This can be done by running one bank of a V engine at a time or by running either the front or the back half of an inline engine. The engine half with the most drop in speed and lowest vacuum has the weak cylinder.

Most modern engine analyzers have switches that can "kill" the ignition of a cylinder at the

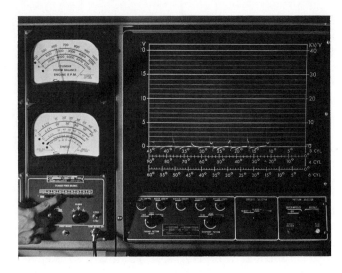

Fig. 10-8 Using a tester with a "kill" switch.

command of the test technician. Some can kill only one at a time, others can kill set groups and still others are designed so the technician can kill the ignition in any sequence he desires.

10-5 POINTS AND CONDENSER

It is the usual practice on each periodic tune-up to change the breaker points and condenser without testing them. The condenser rarely causes trouble and seldom needs to be replaced but the customer has had both points and condenser changed on

Fig. 10-9 Normal wear on high mileage ignition breaker contact points.

tune-ups over the years so he usually expects to have a new condenser installed as part of the periodic tune-up. Breaker points do wear. Their contact surface becomes pitted and the rubbing block wears. In breakerless electronic ignition systems this step is not required when doing a tune-up.

Breaker points are provided as an assembly set. Sometimes a cam lubricant is packaged with them so the cam will receive the correct type of lubricant. Some parts suppliers selling to do-it-yourself consumers put all of the normally replaced ignition components in a single package. These would include points, condenser, spark plugs, rotor, and sometimes a distributor cap.

Two methods can be used to replace points and condensers. The amateur mechanic will usually change them while the distributor is installed in the engine, because he does not want to disturb the basic engine timing. The professional technician will usually remove the distributor from the engine because he can do a better and usually a faster job

Fig. 10-10 Distributor with the cap removed exposing the rotor and points.

of replacing the breaker points and condenser. It also gives him a chance to examine the rest of the distributor for potential problems.

Breaker-point replacement starts with removal of the distributor cap. It is fastened with spring clips, screwdriver lock clips, or screws. The cap is loosened and placed at the side of the distributor with all of the ignition cables remaining in the cap. If the distributor is to be removed from the engine the vacuum-advance unit and rotor position should be noted and its position marked on the distributor housing so that it can be reinstalled in the same position after the points and condenser are installed. The primary lead is removed from the coil and the vacuum hose from the vacuum-advance nipple, then the distributor hold-down clamp is removed so that the distributor can be pulled straight out of its engine opening. Heavy internal engine deposits will sometimes make distributor removal difficult. Careless prying can break the housing and bend the shaft. As some model distributors are removed the distributor shaft will turn a small amount as a result of angled-drive gear teeth. This should be noted and marked on the housing to ease reinstalling the distributor. The following point changing procedure will be the same if the distributor is in the engine or if it is on the bench.

The distributor rotor is removed. On distributors having the centrifugal mechanical advance below the breaker points, the rotor is merely pulled off the shaft. Two screws will have to be removed from the rotor to free the rotor from distributors having the mechanical advance mechanism above the breaker points. If the rotor tip or distributor cap electrodes show excessive burning they should be replaced with new parts, especially if the engine has been misfiring prior to the distributor service. Contact breaker points are exposed when the rotor is removed on most distributors. Some distributors require the removal of a metal shield dust cover to expose the points.

The primary wire and condenser are attached to the breaker points at a single junction. The junction may have a screw or a bolt and nut, or it may be held by a spring pressure push fit. The junction is separated and the single hold-down screw is removed so the points can be lifted from the distributor. If the condenser is to be replaced it can also be removed by taking out one hold-down screw. After wiping the cam a new condenser and breaker

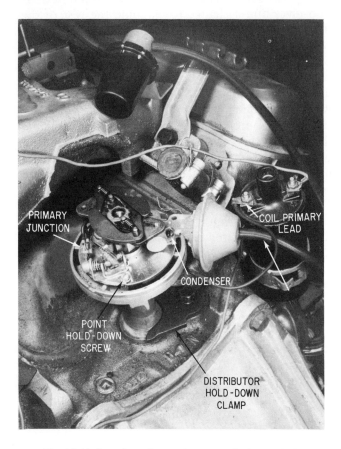

Fig. 10-11 Location of parts that are used when replacing the points and condenser.

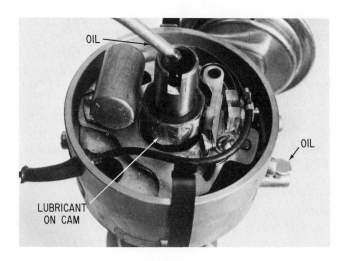

Fig. 10-12. Lubricating points on a distributor.

point set can be installed in the reverse order used to remove them. If a screw is dropped into the distributor the screw must be retrieved because it will break the distributor or distributor drive when it jams within the distributor. Cam lubricant should be wiped smoothly over the cam surface and a drop of oil should be put on the felt plug inside the cam. Excessive lubrication will get on the points and cause them to burn. The distributor bearings should be oiled if an oiler cap is used on the distributor. Most modern distributor bearings have permanent lubrication or are lubricated with motor oil from inside the engine.

When a distributor is in good mechanical condition the ignition point dwell will be correct if the point gap is correct. A point gap between 0.016 in. and 0.018 in. will allow the engine to start, and will usually place the dwell within the correct range. Some four-cylinder engines require a break-

er point gap of 0.025 in. The gap is adjusted while the breaker-point rubbing block is on the highest part of one of the breaker-cam lobes. To prevent accidentally putting dirt between the points, most technicians adjust the points with dwell rather than using a thickness gauge between the points.

Breaker-point sets are usually adjusted properly for maximum service. They should be checked for point contact alignment and for spring tension. Contacts can be aligned by carefully bending the stationary contact to align it with movable contacts. Point spring tension of 19 to 23 oz is checked with a spring scale. Tension can be increased by pushing the point spring into the holding screw, and it can be reduced by sliding the spring from the holding screw. After any point adjustment the gap or dwell should be rechecked. In a professional shop the centrifugal and vacuum-advance mechanisms would be checked at this time. Details of these checks are beyond the scope of this book.

The rotor should be installed. If the distributor is out of the engine the rotor should be turned to the same position it was in when the distributor was removed. With the vacuum-advance unit correctly positioned, the distributor can be installed and engaged with the drive mechanism. The distributor will be close to the correct timing with the engine to allow starting if the engine has not been rotated. The primary wire can then be connected with the coil.

10-6 CARBURETION

Carburetor service is one of the mechanical checks done during a *major* tune-up. The carburetor is disassembled, cleaned, and reassembled using new

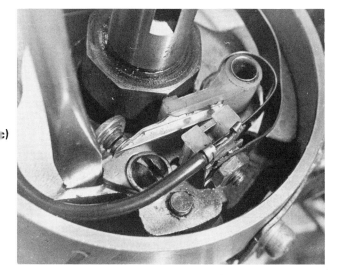

Fig. 10-13 Point gap adjustment. (a) Gap is adjusted with the rubbing block on the high point of the cam, (b) point adjustment with an allen wrench, (c) adjustment with a screwdriver in the notches.

Fig. 10-14 Measuring breaker point spring tension.

parts from a repair kit. Carburetor repair kits are available from a simple gasket set to a complete rebuilding kit that includes almost all new jetting and calibrating components. The most popular carburetor repair kits used for tune-up have new gaskets, an inlet float valve, an acceleration pump, check valves, and assembly clips. The carburetor choke should be checked while the carburetor is cold to see that it is fully closed and that the linkages operate freely before the engine is started. After the carburetor is serviced the engine can be started and the timing set.

10-7 VALVE LASH

Engines with mechanical valve lifters should have the valve lash adjusted as part of a tune-up. The engine must be thoroughly warm when the adjustment is made. On overhead valve engines the rocker covers are removed to expose the rocker arms and adjusters. On flat head engines a side cover is removed to expose the adjusters on the lifters themselves.

Overhead cam engines have their valve lash adjusted when the engine is not running. Valve lash is adjusted by turning the engine to position the cam so that it is not holding the valve, then the clearance is measured with a feeler or thickness gauge. The valve lash spacing is corrected if needed, then the engine is turned to position the next valve

133

Fig. 10-15 Valve lash adjustment. (a) Wedge adjusters on an overhead cam engine, (b) adjustment on a ball-stud rocker arm, (c) adjustment on a shaft rocker arm.

for adjustment. This sequence is followed until valve lash is adjusted on all valves.

The valve lash on overhead valve engines with rocker arms is adjusted with the engine idling. Some engines tend to throw oil from the rocker assemblies when they idle with the rocker covers off. Oil deflectors are available commercially and can be used to help keep the engine clean. Some technicians cut the top out of an old rocker cover and install it as a deflector when they adjust valve lash. With the engine running at slow idle the correct thickness feeler gauge is slipped between the valve tip and the rocker arm pad. The clearance should be adjusted to provide an even pull while the engine is idling. Of course, the feeler gauge cannot move dur-

ing the time the valve is open so it moves with a jerky motion. Step feeler gauges are made especially for valve lash adjustments. The gauge step is 0.002 in. (0.05 mm). If the specification calls for a valve lash or clearance of 0.010 in. (0.25 mm), a step gauge of 0.009 in. (0.225 mm) and 0.011 in. (0.275 mm) would be used. The 0.009 in. (0.225 mm) part should fit between the valve tip and the rocker arm but the 0.011 in. (0.275 mm) part should not. After adjustment, securely set the jam nuts when they are used. After all the clearances have been set the valve lash should be rechecked.

While the rocker covers are off and the engine is warm a number of manufacturers recommend rechecking the cylinder head bolt torque by follow-

12

Engine Lubrication Systems and Service

Lubricating oil is often called the life blood of an engine. It circulates through passages in the engine that carry it to all of the rubbing surfaces. The main job of the oil is to form a film between these surfaces and keep them from touching. This action minimizes friction and wear within the engine. The lubricant has useful secondary functions. Cool lubricant picks up heat from the hot engine parts and takes it to the oil pan where it is cooled as air moves past the outside surface of the pan. The oil flow also carries wear particles from the rubbing surfaces to the pan where they can be drained from the engine so the particles will cause no further damage within the engine. Oil between the engine parts cushions the parts from shock as the combustion charge forces the piston down.

The lubricant used for motor oil must have properties that meet the engine requirements. The most important property of the motor oil is its thickness at normal engine operating temperatures. If the oil is too light it will rapidly leak from the bearing clearances, allowing the parts to contact. This results in scoring of the engine parts. When the oil is too heavy the oil drag between the rubbing surfaces will require excessive engine power. This characteristic is most noticeable when one compares the cranking speed of a cold to a warm engine.

Secondary properties, usually in the form of additives, are put into the oil by the motor oil producers to provide the oil with an ability to clean the engine, minimize scuffing, reduce rusting, resist oxidation, and maintain the oil viscosity characteristics as the temperature changes. The oil should be replaced when it gets dirty or when its properties no longer protect the engine.

12-1 LUBRICATION PRINCIPLES

Lubrication between two moving surfaces results from an oil film that builds up to separate the surfaces and support the load. To understand this principle, consider how slippery a floor seems to be when a liquid is spilled on it. The liquid, either water or oil, supports a person's weight until it is squeezed out from under his feet. If oil were put on a flat surface and a heavy block pushed across this surface, the block would slide more easily than if it were pushed across a dry surface. The reason for this is that a wedge-shaped oil film is built up between the moving block and the surface. This wedge-shaped film is thicker at the front or leading edge than at the rear. If the block were to be held still, the oil would be gradually squeezed out from under the block and the block would settle down on the surface. As soon as the block starts to move again, the wedge-shaped oil film will be re-established.

The force required to push the block across a surface is dependent upon the block weight, how fast it moves, and the thickness or viscosity of the oil. If the block is heavy, it will quickly squeeze

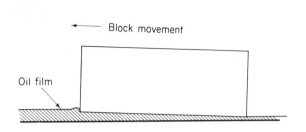

Fig. 12-1 Wedge-shaped hydrodynamic oil film.

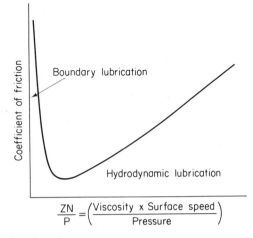

$$\frac{ZN}{P} = \left(\frac{Viscosity \times Surface\ speed}{Pressure}\right)$$

Fig. 12-2 ZN/P curve.

the oil from under the surface. The faster the block is moved, the less time is available for oil to be squeezed out, so a heavier load can be supported as speed is increased. This principle is used in water skiing.

The other factor in an oil film's ability to support a load is the oil's thickness. Thin oil would squeeze out faster than thick oil; therefore, the thick oil can support a much greater load. The oil can be too thick. If the oil becomes too thick it becomes sluggish, so that it will require great effort to move the block over the oil. If the oil is too thin, the block is not supported completely and the block will drag slightly on the surface. For any given block weight and moving speed, there is one oil thickness which requires the least effort to move the block. The force required to move the block divided by the pressure caused by the block weight is called the *coefficient of friction*.

The principle just described is called *hydrodynamic* lubrication. Hydro refers to liquids, as in hydraulics, and dynamic refers to moving materials. Hydrodynamic lubrication occurs when a wedge-shaped film develops in a liquid between two moving surfaces. When this film becomes so thin that the surface high spots touch, it is called boundary lubrication.

As the coefficient of friction increases, it takes more effort to move the block. The least effort is required when the correct wedge-shaped oil film exists. The coefficient of friction will increase during boundary lubrication or when the oil is too thick. This can be shown on the dimensionless graph in Figure 12-2, where the oil thickness or *viscosity* is expressed as Z, the speed at which the block moves across the surface is expressed as N and the pressure caused by the block weight is expressed as P. The coefficient of friction is minimum for one value of ZN/P. If the load P is increased, the value of ZN/P is reduced and the film

moves left toward boundary conditions. Any increase in speed will increase ZN/P and move the expression to the right. It takes more effort to increase the speed while using the same viscosity and load. For any constant speed and load, the oil film is dependent upon the oil viscosity. Viscosity is oil's most important property.

Flat surface lubrication only exists in a few places in automotive engines. Some of these are thrust bearings, valve tips and lifter bases on the cam. Most moving surfaces are similar to flat bearing surfaces, but they are somewhat curved. They still use the same hydrodynamic lubrication principles just described. These surfaces may be curved in one way to form a cylinder wall, lifter bore, or valve guide. When curved in the other direction, they are used as main, connecting rod and camshaft bearings.

The engine oil pressure system delivers a continuous supply of oil to the lightly loaded portion of bearing surfaces. Hydrodynamic lubrication takes over as the shaft rotates in the bearing to produce a wedge-shaped hydrodynamic oil film that is curved around the bearing. This film supports the bearing and, where using oil of the correct viscosity, will reduce the turning effort to a minimum. Changes in viscosity, speed, or load affect the bearing lubrication in the same way they do with a block moving on a flat surface just described.

A crankshaft main bearing will be used to describe typical bearing lubrication. When the engine is not running, the crankshaft pushes much of the oil from around it as it settles to the bottom of the bearing. As the starter is cranked, the crankshaft tries to roll up the bearing side wall. If some surface oil remains on the bearing, the shaft will slide back to the bottom of the bearing when it hits this oil. Continued turning will repeat this sequence of climbing and sliding back. The sequence continues until the oil pump supplies fresh oil to the bearing journal. The shaft continues to try to climb up the bearing wall; however, it now grabs oil instead of the bearing surface. This pulls oil around the shaft, forming a curved wedge-shaped oil film that supports the crankshaft in the bearing. Most bearing wear occurs during the initial start and continues until a hydrodynamic film is established.

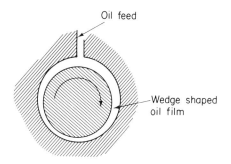

Fig. 12-3 Wedge-shaped oil film around a journal bearing.

A continuous new oil supply is required to maintain the oil film because oil will leak from the side of the bearing. This oil leakage flushes contaminants from the bearing as well as removes heat that is generated in the bearing.

One of the engine lubrication system's functions is to maintain a positive and continuous oil supply to the bearings. Engine oil pressure is high enough to get the oil to bearings with sufficient force to produce adequate oil flow for proper cooling. Normal engine oil pressure range is from 30 to 60 psi while the hydrodynamic film pressures developed in the high pressure areas of the engine bearings may be over 1000 psi. The relatively low engine oil pressures, obviously, couldn't support these engine loads without hydrodynamic lubrication.

12-2 PROPERTIES OF MOTOR OIL

The most important motor oil property is its thickness or viscosity. As an oil cools, it thickens and as it heats up, it gets thinner; therefore, its viscosity changes with temperature. The oil must have a low enough viscosity at low temperatures to allow the engine to start. Thick oil at low temperatures causes a very high coefficient of friction as can be seen on the right side of the ZN/P curve in Figure 12-2. If this coefficient of friction becomes too great, the cold engine will not have enough energy

to carry over from one firing impulse to the next. When this happens, the engine will not start. There is a maximum oil viscosity that will allow an engine to start at any specific temperature. On the other end of the scale, with the engine hot, the oil thins and the viscosity lowers. If the viscosity becomes too low, boundary lubrication will occur and the coefficient of friction will increase, as is shown on the left end of the ZN/P curve. Motor oil must have its viscosity between these two extremes. It must be thin enough to allow the engine to start when cold and it must still have enough body or viscosity to develop the correct hydrodynamic lubrication film when it gets to its normal operating temperature. An index of the change in viscosity between the cold and hot viscosity is called *viscosity index*. All oils thin as they get hot; however, oils with a high viscosity index thin less than oils with a low viscosity index.

The viscosity of an oil is determined by one of several types of viscosimeters. The oldest and most familiar viscosity measurement device is the Saybolt viscosimeter. It consists of an accurately machined brass tube with a calibrated opening in its bottom called a Universal orifice. The tube is surrounded by a bath that is maintained at the test temperature. In operation, the tube is fitted with a stopper at its lower end, then filled with the sample oil. It is given time to stabilize at the test temperature. When the

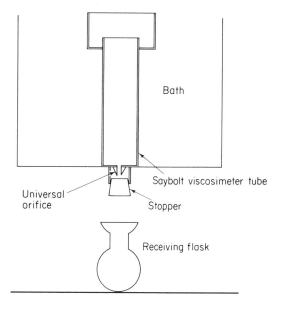

Fig. 12-4 Line drawing of a Saybolt viscosimeter.

test temperature is reached, the stopper is pulled from the tube, allowing the sample to flow through the Universal orifice. The viscosity from this test is reported as *Saybolt Universal Seconds* (SUS). Minimum coefficient of friction occurs when the viscosity is from 30 to 40 SUS at the operating temperature.

Two test temperatures are used to classify motor oils, 0°F (-18°C) and 210°F (99°C). The 0°F (-18°C) test indicates the oil's viscosity at low temperatures and the 210°F (99°C) test indicates the oil viscosity at normal engine operating temperatures.

Viscosity testing by the Saybolt viscosimeter is quite time consuming and is being replaced by alternate viscosity test methods. The 210°F (99°C) high temperature test is done using a test procedure for opaque liquids and the results are reported in *centistokes*, the designation for kinematic viscosity. In this test, a measured amount of oil sample is drawn into a glass viscosimeter tube, then placed in a 210°F (99°C) bath. The top of the sample is drawn slightly above two test lines. The time it takes the sample to drain from one test line to the next is measured in seconds. The seconds are multiplied by the viscosimeter correction factor to get the viscosity value in centistokes. This test may be repeated a number of times for accuracy without

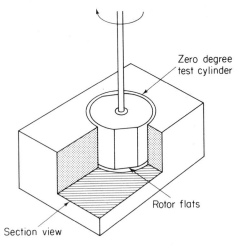

Fig. 12-6 Line drawing of a cold cranking simulator.

draining the viscosimeter tube. It is easier and faster to use than a Saybolt viscosimeter.

Another test procedure uses a Cold Cranking Simulator that is replacing the Saybolt viscosimeter for 0°F (-18°C) tests. The Cold Cranking Simulator has a rotor, with two flats, that is placed in a cylinder. The cylinder is then filled with the sample and the whole unit cooled to 0°F (-18°C). At this test temperature, the rotor is turned by a constant speed motor. The effort required to turn the rotor is reported in *centipoise*, a measurement of absolute viscosity. Here again, the test is quicker and simpler than the Saybolt viscosity test.

12-3 MOTOR OIL IDENTIFICATION

Motor oil viscosity is graded by SAE viscosity numbers. Each SAE number includes a range of viscosities measured by one of the previously described test procedures. The SAE (Society of Automotive Engineers) has used 210°F (99°C) as the test temperature to represent the oil viscosity in a warm engine. SAE 20 is the thinnest motor oil grade measured at this temperature and SAE 50 is the thickest grade, with SAE 30 and 40 between. These viscosity grade numbers cover the entire 210°F (99°C) viscosity range of oils used in engines. SAE uses 0°F (-18°C) as a second test temperature to rate the winter cold cranking characteristic caused by the thickness of the oil at low temperature. At this temperature SAE 5W oil grade is the thinnest followed by SAE 10W and 20W as the oil thickness increases. Notice that the number is followed by the letter *W* when the oil is tested at 0°F (-18°C) and no letter is used when the oil is tested at 210°F (99°C).

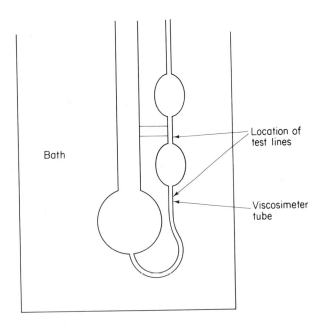

Fig. 12-5 Line drawing of a glass kinematic viscosimeter tube.

SAE Viscosity Number	Viscosity Units	At 0°		At 210°	
		min	max	min	max
5 W	Centipoises SUS	– –	1,200 6,000	– –	– –
10 W	Centipoises SUS	1,200 6,000	2,400 12,000	– –	– –
20 W	Centipoises SUS	2,400 12,000	9,600 48,000	– –	– –
20	Centistokes SUS	– –	– –	5.7 45	9.6 58
30	Centistokes SUS	– –	– –	9.6 58	12.9 70
40	Centistokes SUS	– –	– –	12.9 70	16.8 85
50	Centistokes SUS	– –	– –	16.8 85	22.7 110

Fig. 12-7 Table comparing viscosity to the SAE numbers (*1974 SAE Handbook,* Society of Automotive Engineers).

cold. This becomes especially critical in northern winters. When the engine is running for long periods at turnpike speeds the oil operating temperature is nearly the same in both winter and summer. The oil must be thin enough to allow the engine to start when it is cold and still have sufficient viscosity to protect the engine when it becomes hot. Multigrade oils have been designed to meet the wide operating temperature range requirements of modern automobile engines driven on modern highways.

In use oil becomes contaminated with combustion products that slip past the piston rings; with particles that wear from within the engine; and from changes that occur as the oil contacts hot en-

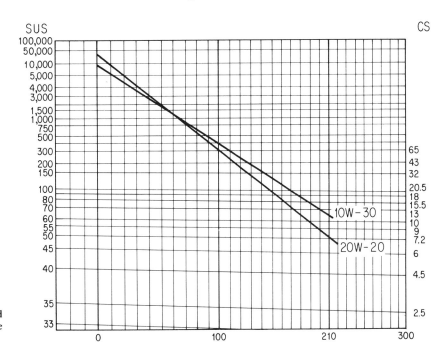

Fig. 12-8 Viscosity plotted on a standard viscosity-temperature chart (Courtesy of the Society for Testing Materials).

When an oil is tested at only one of these temperatures it is called a single grade or straight grade oil. For example, either an SAE 10W or an SAE 30 oil would be considered a single straight grade oil. If the oil viscosity is measured at both test temperatures the oil is called a multigrade oil. For example, SAE 20W-20 and SAE 10W-40 are both multigrade oils.

If an engine operated continuously at a single temperature an oil viscosity could be selected that would give maximum protection and minimum friction or drag. Automobile engines must start

gine parts, called *oxidation*. Detergent-dispersant additives are put into the oil to keep oxidation products suspended until they are removed from the engine as the oil is changed. Antioxidants, rust inhibitors, etc. are added to the oil to reduce oxidation and protect the engine.

Oils are given an API (American Petroleum Institute) oil performance and service classification designation to indicate to the operator how the oil is expected to protect his engine.

To be rated for API designation motor oils are run in full scale engines under closely controlled

Fig. 12-9 Identification marking on a can of motor oil.

test procedures that will measure the ability of the oil to keep the camshaft and lifters from scuffing, and its tendency to produce minimum varnish, sludge, and rust within the engine.

Motor oils available in service stations are given API designations SA, SB, SC, etc. The series designation is open ended so that as new oil requirements become apparent and are met, new API designations can be added. In general, SA oils have no additives and provide protection only where operating conditions are very mild. As the letter designation goes through the alphabet the protection provided by the oil increases. Each engine manufacturer specifies the service requirements needed for the engine he manufactures. At the time of this writing the SE designation was the standard service recommendation for automotive engines.

Bulk commercial oils designated especially for diesel-engine protection are called C series oils (CA, CB, CC, etc.). They are required to meet tests similar to the S series tests in full scale engines. Some oils have several API classifications on the container. This means that these oils have been tested by all of the test sequences required for each classification listed and that they may be used wherever any one of the classifications is specified by the engine manufacturer.

Racing-type motor oils are formulated from select grades of petroleum stock for extremely high temperature service. Chemicals are added to control the build-up of high temperature varnish deposits. High temperature oil oxidation is retarded by the addition of chemicals that also provide anti-wear characteristics. Ashless detergent-dispersants are used to suspend the high temperature sludge-forming compounds as well as minimize surface ignition tendencies. The oil has an inhibitor that reduces the tendency to foam at high engine speeds used in racing. Racing oils with the proper oil performance and engine service classifications will provide satisfactory performance in normal street use when the outside air temperature remains above 32°F (0°C), but they will not be better in this type of service than SE motor oils designed for normal street use.

12-4 MOTOR OIL ADDITIVES

Additives are used in motor oils for three different reasons: (1) to replace some properties removed during refining, (2) to reinforce some of the oil's natural properties, and (3) to provide the oil with new properties it did not originally have. Oils from some petroleum oil fields require more and different additives than oils from other fields. Additives are usually classified according to the property they add to the oil.

Antioxidants reduce the high temperature contaminants. They prevent the formation of varnish, reduce bearing corrosion, and particle formation.

Corrosion preventatives reduce acid formation that would cause bearing corrosion.

Detergents and dispersants prevent low temperature sludge binders from forming and break the sludge particles into a finely divided state. The particles will stay in suspension in the oil to be removed from the engine with the oil at the drain period.

Extreme pressure and anti-wear additives form a chemical film that prevents metal to metal seizure anytime boundary lubrication exists.

Viscosity index improvers are used to reduce viscosity change as the oil temperature changes.

Pour point depressants coat the wax crystals in the oil so they will not stick together and the oil will then be able to flow at lower temperatures.

A number of other oil additives may be used to modify the oil. These include rust preventatives, metal deactivators, water repellents, emulsifiers, dyes, color stabilizers, odor control agents, and foam inhibitors.

The oil producer must be careful to check the compatibility of the oil additives he uses. A number of chemicals that will help each other can be used for each of the additive requirements. However, with improper additive selection, the additives may oppose each other and lose their benefit to the oil. Each oil producer balances the additives in his oil to provide an oil with desirable properties that meet the engine's needs.

Additives available at service stations, or *proprietary* additives, generally cannot add any needed desirable property to the oil that it does not already possess. It is even possible that these additives may neutralize some of the additives already in the oil, thus degrading the oil instead of improving it. The procedure usually recommended by the engine manufacturer is to use only SE oil without additional proprietary additives. When adding oil between changes, it is a good practice to add the same brand and grade of oil that is already in the engine, thus minimizing the chance of having conflicting additives.

12-5 ENGINE LUBRICATION SYSTEM

Automobile engines use a *wet sump* in their lubrication system. The sump is the lowest part of the system and, in automobile engines, this is the oil pan. It is called a wet sump because it holds the oil supply. Some racing and industrial engines use a *dry sump*. A scavenger pump in dry sump engines draws the oil out of a relatively small sump and returns it to a separate oil supply tank. The engine oil pump pulls oil from this oil supply tank to feed the engine lubrication system.

Production automobile engines have full pressure oil systems. Oil pressure is maintained by an oil pump that picks up motor oil through a passage

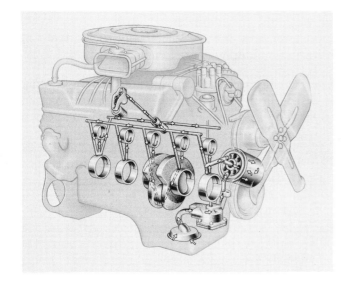

Fig. 12-10 A typical engine lubricating system with the valve train lubricated through the push rods (Ford Motor Company).

from an inlet screen in the oil pan and forces it into the lubrication system under pressure.

Oil Pressure. The oil pump is usually driven from a gear on the camshaft. In most engines, the distributor drive gear meshes with the camshaft gear. The oil pump is driven from the end of the distributor shaft. Some engines have a short shaft-gear that meshes with the cam gear to drive both the distributor and oil pump. Occasionally, an engine is built that uses separate gears on the distributor and on the oil pump. Both mate with the same cam gear. With these drive methods, the pump turns at one-half engine speed. In one engine type the oil pump is driven by the front of the crankshaft and, obviously, turns at engine speed.

Fig. 12-11 Typical oil pump drive method.

In engines with full pressure lubricating systems, maximum pressure is limited with a *pressure regulator* or *relief valve*. If a pressure regulator valve were not used, the engine oil pressure would continue to increase as the engine speed increased. Maximum pressure is usually limited to a pressure that will deliver an adequate quantity of lubricating oil to engine locations where it is required. Three to six gallons of lubricating oil per minute are required for normal lubrication. After the oil enters the bearing or splashes on surfaces requiring lubrication, oil films are maintained by hydrodynamic forces. Excessive oil pressure requires more horsepower and provides no better lubrication. High oil pressure and resulting high rates of oil flow may, in some cases, tend to erode engine bearings.

The pressure regulator is located downstream from the pressure side of the oil pump. It generally consists of a spring-loaded piston and, in a few cases, a spring-loaded ball. When oil pressure reaches the regulated pressure, it will force the regulator valve back against the calibrated spring, compressing it as the valve is forced back. This allows a controlled "leak" from the pressure system at a rate that will maintain the set regulated oil pressure. Any change in the regulator valve spring pressure will change the regulated oil pressure; higher spring pressures will produce higher maximum oil pressures. In most engines, the oil that is released by the regulator valve is routed to the inlet side of the oil pump to be recirculated through the pump. The regulator valve is, therefore, usually located in the oil pump housing or pump cover. This method of oil flow from the regulator valve prevents foaming and excessive oil agitation so that a solid stream of lubricating oil will be delivered by the pump.

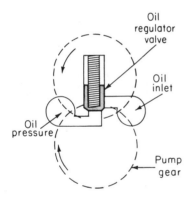

Fig. 12-12 Line drawing of an oil pressure regulator located in the oil pump cover.

Oil Filter. Oil leaving the pump flows to the oil filter where foreign particles are trapped, allowing only clean oil to flow into the engine. Filters are designed to trap large particles that could damage engine bearings. Very fine particles flow through the filter. These particles are so fine that they can get between engine clearances and do no damage. As the filter traps particles, the holes in the filter become partly plugged. As they plug the filter traps even smaller particles, thus doing a better filtering job. This better filtering, however, restricts oil flow and this could result in bearing oil starvation. All filters or filter adapters have a by-pass check valve so that if the filter becomes plugged, oil can bypass the plugged filter and go directly

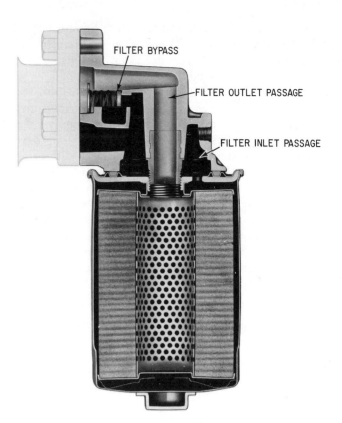

Fig. 12-13 Cross section of a typical oil filter (AC Division, General Motors Corporation).

into the engine. The by-pass valve is set to open at a pressure of 5-15 psi difference between the filter inlet and outlet, depending on the engine design and the normal pressure drop across the filter element.

Filters or filter adapters are also supplied with a check valve that keeps the filter full when the engine is stopped. It keeps the oil from leaking back through the oil pump into the pan, and so the oil pump remains primed. This will provide rapid oil pressure buildup when the engine starts.

Oil Passages. From the filter, oil goes through a drilled hole that intersects with a drilled main oil gallery or longitudinal header. Inline engines use one oil gallery. V engines may use two main galleries or one main gallery and two valve-lifter galleries. Drilled passages through the engine block bulkheads allow the oil to go from the main oil gallery to the main and cam bearings. In some engines, oil goes to the cam bearings first, then to the main bearings, while other engines direct the oil to the main bearings first, then to the cam bearings. The crankshaft is drilled to allow oil from the oil groove in the main bearings to be directed to the connecting rod bearings.

The oil gallery may intersect or have drilled passages to the valve lifter bores to lubricate the

Fig. 12-14 Oil cross hole drilled in a crankshaft.

lifters. When hydraulic lifters are used, the gallery oil pressure keeps refilling them. On some engines, oil from the lifters goes up the center of a hollow pushrod to lubricate the pushrod ends, the rocker arm pivot, and the valve stem tip. In other engines, an oil passage is drilled from the gallery or from a cam bearing to the block deck, where it matches with a gasket hole and a hole drilled in the head to carry the oil to a rocker assembly. Some engines use an enlarged head bolt hole to carry lubricating oil around the head bolt to the rocker arm shaft. Holes in the bottom of the rocker arm shaft lubri-

cate the rocker arm pivot. Often, holes are drilled in cast rocker arms to carry oil to the pushrod end and to the valve tip. Rocker arm assemblies need only a surface coating of oil, and so the size of the oil passage to the rocker assembly is reduced using restrictions or metered openings.

Oil that seeps from the rocker assemblies is returned to the oil pan through drain holes. These oil drain holes are often placed so that the oil drains on the camshaft or on cam drive gears to splash lubricate them.

12-6 MOTOR OIL REQUIREMENTS

The engine requires an oil that, when cold, will flow freely enough to allow the engine to crank and start. If the oil is too thick, such as it might be in a cold engine in a northern winter, the engine will not start. As the engine warms, the oil thins. It must not become so thin that it cannot form the required oil film between moving parts.

The operator has two means to keep track of engine lubrication. He has a dip stick on the engine to check the oil quantity. A standard quantity of oil is needed in the engine to keep the oil pump inlet screen covered with oil under all driving conditions and to allow sufficient time for the oil to cool

Fig. 12-15 Oil feed passages drilled through the head (Chrysler Motors Corporation).

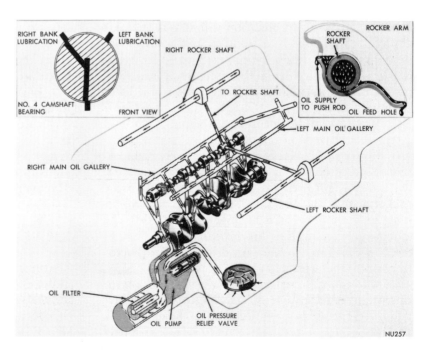

before it recirculates through the engine. The operator also has an oil pressure gauge or minimum pressure red light to indicate the proper functioning of the lubricating system.

Oil pressure is built up as the oil pump attempts to push more oil through the engine oil system than can leak through the engine bearing oil-clearances, thus assuring a constant positive oil supply to the bearings. Oil pressure is reduced if the bearing oil-clearances become so great that the oil flows easily through the bearing oil-clearances. It is also reduced if the oil pump becomes so worn that oil slips around the pump gears and does not go into the engine oil system. If the oil becomes *very* thin, through the use of the wrong oil grade or when it becomes unusually hot, the oil will flow easily through the engine oil system without developing sufficient pressure. Low oil pressure is always an indication of a problem or an impending failure. It should never be ignored. The cause of low oil pressure should be determined and corrected before serious engine damage occurs.

The greatest lubrication demand in engines is usually considered to be the bearings. Their lubrication is necessary for maximum service life of the engine; however, their lubrication is quite simple and is easily met with properly designed bearings using oil with the correct viscosity.

The highest unit pressures actually occur between the cam lobes and valve lifters. Much of modern motor oil formulation is based on the oil's ability to minimize lifter scuffing and wear. Cam lobes are not lubricated with positive pressure, but rely on oil thrown from the connecting rods and on oil that drains back from the rocker and lifter chambers.

Valve assemblies, pistons, piston pins, oil pump distributor drive, and cam drives only require a surface film of oil. The loads are relatively light, so that oil received from splash is usually adequate. Oil under slight pressure is usually directed to the rocker arms. The amount of pressure is not important, only that the oil is positively delivered to the moving surface needing lubrication. Some engines direct an oil flow to the cam drive. This oil helps to cushion the drive and reduce noise.

Automobile engines also use engine oil to operate hydraulic valve lifters. This places another and different kind of requirement on the engine oil. Hydraulic lifters are manufactured with extremely

close fitting parts, to minimize leakage. Small foreign particles that get into these clearances could cause the lifter to malfunction. The engine oil must keep the lifter clean, limiting deposit formation that would cause lifter sticking.

12-7 LUBRICATING SYSTEM SERVICE

As oil is used, it deteriorates and requires changing. Two general types of oil deterioration exist—contamination and breakdown.

Oil may be contaminated with dirt or coolant. The most common type of contamination, however, is from the blow-by gases that work their way past the piston and rings. If crankcase ventilation is poor and the engine is cool, blow-by gases remain in the crankcase and mix with the oil. The undesirable blow-by constituents primarily consist of partially burned fuel and water vapor. Unburned fuel dilutes the oil. The highly acidic water from combustion causes rusting and corrosion. Both combine with polymerized and oxidized hydrocarbons, produced during combustion, undergoing further change in the oil to form sludge "binders" that hold organic solids, inorganic salts, wear particles, and fuel soot together. When these particles get large enough, they drop out of the oil and deposit in the engine as a cold-engine sludge of mayonnaise consistency.

When an engine is run at normal operating temperatures for some time, the oil gets hot and breaks down. Oil breakdown is the result of hot oil combining with oxygen, and is called oxidation. This will eventually form hard carbon and varnish deposits on engine parts when it is allowed to build up over a long period of time. Two hundred and fifty degrees fahrenheit (121°C) is the normal maximum engine oil temperature.

Engine oil additives tend to deteriorate and be used up as the oil is used. When they can no longer do their designed job, the oil loses some of its necessary properties. Engine oils should be changed before sludge develops, before oxidized deposits form, and before the additives lose their effectiveness.

12-8 PERIODIC OIL CHANGES

Oil changes are required to remove the contaminants suspended in the oil and to replace the depleted oil additives. Two bases are used for specifying oil changes, *time* and *mileage*. Deposits build up rapidly over low mileage when the engine is driven on many short trips. In this type of operation the engine is not driven long enough to become sufficiently warm to evaporate moisture condensation in the crankcase, and so moisture gradually builds up, mixes with the oil, and forms sludge. For this reason oil change recommendations give a maximum *time* period (60 or 90 days). When the engine is operated on turnpikes and freeways the oil gets hot and oxidizes to form coke and varnish. Mileage builds up rapidly so the oil change recommendation also includes a maximum *mileage* before an oil change. To keep the engine clean and provide maximum service life the oil should be changed on the time basis or on the mileage basis, *whichever occurs first*. If the recommendations are ignored contaminants will drop out of the oil and form permanent deposits within the engine. Internal deposits insulate to prevent proper heat flow and they can plug passages to prevent oil flow.

The oil SAE grade to be used should be one that is recommended for the air temperature expected before the next oil change. The oil should have a low viscosity to aid in starting during cold weather. At normal operating temperature the oil must have sufficient viscosity to keep friction at a minimum. Multi-grade oil will usually meet these requirements. If the oil viscosity is too low at the engine operating temperature engine oil consumption will be high.

Because there is a wide variety of additives used in motor oils it is usually considered a good practice to avoid mixing brands of oil between oil changes. Mixing SAE grades of the same brand will cause no problem and the resulting viscosity will be somewhere between the two grades being mixed.

Oil change periods recommended by the engine manufacturers are almost twice as long as those recommended by the petroleum industry. The first thought that comes to mind is that the petroleum industry wants a lot of oil to be used so they can earn more profit. This of course may be true, but it is not the reason for their recommended short oil change period. It should be recognized that the automobile manufacturer's recommendations are to his customer, the new car buyer. The typical new car buyer will trade his car for another new one by the time the car has been driven 50,000 miles (80,450 km) and if he follows the automobile manufacturer's recommendations, the car will give him satisfactory service at minimum cost for the mileage. The petroleum industry, on the other hand, recommends an oil change schedule that will provide the maximum engine service life, not just for the first owner. Both are correct. The reason

for the different recommendations are their different objectives.

12-9 OIL DRAIN

The oil can be drained more rapidly from a warm engine than from a cold one. Position a drain pan under the drain plug, then remove the plug with care to avoid contact with hot oil and allow the oil to drain freely. It is not critically important to get every last drop of oil from the engine oil pan because a quantity of used oil still remains in the engine oil passages. While the engine oil is draining the oil plug gasket should be examined. If it appears to be distorted it should be replaced. When the oil stops running and starts to drip, reinstall and tighten the drain plug. Refill the engine with the proper type, grade, and quantity of oil. Restart the engine if a new filter is not required and allow the engine to idle until it develops oil pressure, then check for leaks.

12-10 OIL FILTERS

The oil within the engine is pumped from the oil pan through the filter before it goes into the engine lubricating system passages. The filter is made from either closely packed cloth fibers or a porous paper. Particles of any appreciable size are trapped by the filter. Microscopic particles will flow through the filter pores. These particles are so small that they can flow through the bearing oil film and not touch the surfaces, so they do no damage.

Either the engine or the filter is provided with a by-pass that will allow the oil to go around a plugged filter element if an operator neglects to have the filter changed at the proper time. This allows the engine to be lubricated with dirty oil rather than having no lubrication if the filter becomes plugged. Most engine manufacturers recommend filter changes at every other oil change period. Correct oil filter selection includes the use of a filter with an internal by-pass when the engine is not equipped with one.

Some oil filters have replaceable elements. A long central tube holds the cover over the element and against the engine flange. This tube is removable to enable the technician to replace the filter element. The filter housing is thoroughly cleaned and the new element installed with new seals. The tube should be tightened to the recommended torque to prevent leakage.

Most automobile engines use a sealed spin-on filter. It has the new filtering element sealed in a can that is screwed onto an engine fitting. The spin-on type is more expensive but is much faster and cleaner to use.

If the spin-on filter has been installed properly it can be removed by hand. Filter wrenches are available and should be used in cases where the filter cannot be removed by hand. A drain pan placed below the filter will catch the oil that drips as the old filter is removed. After the filter is removed the sealing surface on the engine should be examined to make sure it is clean and smooth so the new filter will be able to seal properly. The oil seal of the new filter is coated with motor oil and the filter is screwed on by hand. It should be turned an additional one-half to three-quarter turn after the oil seal first touches the engine sealing surface. The engine is restarted and allowed to idle until the filter fills and engine oil pressure is reestablished. With the engine running a check is made for oil leaks around the filter. A final check of the oil level should be made before the filter replacement job is complete.

Periodic replacement of the oil and filter with the recommended oil and correct type filter is the best preventive measure to ensure a long engine life that is free from costly repair bills.

REVIEW QUESTIONS

1. What is an engine sump?

2. How does a dry sump differ from a wet sump system?

3. What turns the oil pump drive gear?

4. Where does oil go after it is released by the regulator valve?

5. What limits maximum oil pump pressure on an engine?

6. Why is a by-pass used in oil filters?

7. How are most oil passages made in an engine?

8. What limits the oil thickness and thinness for use in an engine?

9. Why does the oil pressure drop when large bearing clearances exist?

10. What is the most important oil property?

11. What is the difference between SAE20 oil and SAE20W oil?

12. What oil performance and service classifications are recommended for modern automobile engines?

13. How does racing oil differ from multigrade SE motor oils?

14. Why are oil changes recommended?

15. What are the two bases used for oil change requirements?

16. Which is the better oil change recommendation—the engine manufacturer's or the oil company's?

17. Why is it not important to drain every drop of oil from an engine during an oil change?

18. What is important when selecting oil filter replacement for an engine?

13

Engine Cooling

The primary function of the automotive engine cooling system is to maintain the normal operating temperature of the block and head. Coolant flow is held at a minimum during warmup until the normal engine temperature is reached, then the coolant flow is gradually increased, as required, to maintain the normal engine operating temperature. If the engine operating temperature is too low, scuffing and wear rates will increase within the engine. If temperature is too high, hard deposits will form that can cause part-sticking and passage-clogging. Operating the engine at normal temperatures minimizes these problems and provides the engine with maximum service life.

Two types of cooling systems, air and liquid, are used in passenger cars. A few domestic passenger cars have used air cooling and some import passenger cars presently use air cooling systems. Current domestic passenger cars use liquid cooling systems. The liquid coolant removes the excess heat from the engine and carries it to a radiator where it releases the heat to the air.

Air cooling systems are limited to a few low-horsepower automobiles. They are used exclusively on small utility engines, and on motorcycles and on piston engined aircraft. The air-cooled engine transfers heat from the cylinder directly to the air through fins that are a part of the cylinder. In automotive applications the cylinders and cooling fins are surrounded with shrouds, ducts, and baffles that direct fan air around the hot finned cylinders.

In some cases thermostatically controlled doors in the ducts are used to control the engine temperature. Additional engine cooling is usually supplied with an oil radiator that cools the motor oil.

Most automobiles use a liquid cooling system. The cooling liquid enters the coolant pump, also called a *water pump*. The pump delivers coolant to the coolant passages in the engine block, where it flows around the cylinders. Coolant flows from the block to the head. Here it is collected at a common point where the thermostat is located. A small amount of coolant is by-passed around the thermostat and returned to the engine during warm-up to maintain equal temperatures throughout the engine. When coolant becomes warm the thermostat opens, allowing coolant to flow to one of the radiator tanks: to the top tank on a down-flow radiator, or to one of the side tanks of a cross-flow radiator. Coolant flows through small tubes in the radiator. These tubes are soldered to metal fins forming the radiator core. Heat transfers from the coolant to the metal fins, to be further transferred into the air that moves through the radiator core. The coolant is a transfer medium that carries heat from the combustion chamber to the air and out of the vehicle. Cooled liquid coolant returns from the other radiator tank to the pump to be forced back through the cooling system circuit. A vehicle traveling at highway speeds and pulling a trailer may pump over 50 gallons (190 liters) of coolant a minute through the cooling system.

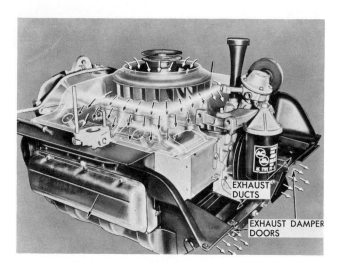

Fig. 13-1 An air cooled engine (Chevrolet Motor Division, General Motors Corporation).

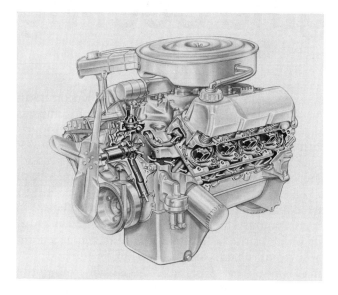

Fig. 13-2 A liquid cooled engine (Ford Motor Company).

13-1 COOLING SYSTEM REQUIREMENTS

The cooling system must allow the engine to warm up to the required operating temperature as rapidly as possible, then maintain that temperature. It must be able to do this when the outside air temperature is as low as -30°F (-35°C) and as high as 110°F (45°C). This will allow proper carburetion, provide satisfactory oil viscosity, and give the correct part fits and clearances within the engine.

Peak combustion temperatures in the engine cycle run from 4000°F to 6000°F (2220°C to 3330°C). They will average from 1200°F to 1700°F (650°C to 925°C) throughout the operating cycle. Continued temperatures as high as this would weak-en engine parts, so heat must be removed from the engine. The cooling system keeps the head and cylinder wall at a temperature within their physical strength limits.

Low Temperature Requirements. Minimum engine operating temperatures are critical for proper engine operation. When the temperature is too low, there is insufficient heat to properly vaporize the fuel mixture so that extra fuel is necessary to provide satisfactory engine performance. The heavy portion of the gasoline does not vaporize and remains as unburned fuel. Cool engine surfaces quench part of the combustion, leaving partially burned fuel as soot. The cool engine surfaces also cool the burned by-products, condensing moisture that is produced during combustion. The unburned fuel, soot and moisture go past the piston rings as blow-by gases, washing oil from the cylinder wall and diluting the oil in the pan. This exposes the cylinder wall and piston rings to excessive scuffing and wear.

Gasoline is a hydrocarbon with additives to reduce detonation, surface ignition, corrosion, gum formation, and ice formation. Some of the anti-knock additives contain chlorine and bromine. Gasoline combustion is a rapid oxidation process in which heat is released as the hydrocarbon fuel chemically combines with oxygen from the air. For each gallon of fuel used, a moisture equivalent of a gallon of water is produced. It is a part of this moisture that condenses and gets into the oil pan, along with unburned fuel and soot, and causes sludge formation.

The condensed moisture combines with unburned hydrocarbons and additives to form carbonic acid, sulfuric acid, nitric acid, hydrobromic acid, and hydrochloric acid. These acids are chiefly responsible for engine wear by causing corrosion and rust within the engine. Rust occurs rapidly when the coolant temperature is below 130°F (55°C). Below 110°F (45°C), water from the combustion process will actually accumulate in the oil. High cylinder wall wear rates occur anytime the coolant temperature is below 150°F (65°C).

High Temperature Requirements. Maximum temperature limits are also required to protect the engine. High temperatures oxidize the engine oil. This breaks the oil down, producing hard carbon and varnish. If high temperatures are allowed to continue, they will lead to plugged piston rings and stuck hydraulic valve lifters. High temperatures reduce the oil's viscosity, that is, they thin the oil. This may allow metal-to-metal contact within the engine, which will cause high friction, loss of power, and rapid wear. Reduced oil viscosity allows the oil to get past the piston rings and through valve guides into the combustion chamber to cause excessive oil consumption.

The combustion process is very sensitive to temperature. High coolant temperatures raise the combustion temperatures to a point that detonation and pre-ignition may occur and, if allowed to continue for any period of time, will lead to engine damage.

Normal Temperatures. Between low temperature and high temperature extremes, there is a

normal operating temperature range. The minimum normal temperature, controlled by a thermostat, has been gradually increased from 160°F to 180-190°F (72°C to 80-87°C). Some engines run with a minimum temperature as high as 200°F (95°C). The maximum possible temperature on liquid-cooled engines is limited by the coolant's boiling point and radiator's capacity. On air-cooled engines, it is limited by the air temperature and flow rate. Engine operating temperature should be kept between these extremes, usually at the minimum temperature, for proper engine operation and maximum service life.

13-2 COOLANT

Water was the first coolant used to maintain the temperature of internal combustion engines. Water can carry more heat in the same volume than any other coolant material at the same temperature. Water does have some limitations however. It freezes at temperatures encountered in many locations during the winter months. Antifreeze mater-

(a)

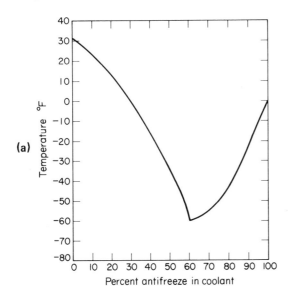

Fig. 13-3 Effect of glycol–water mixture. (a) Freezing temperature, (b) boiling temperature, (c) specific heat.

(b)

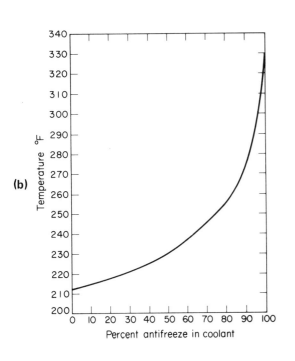

(c)

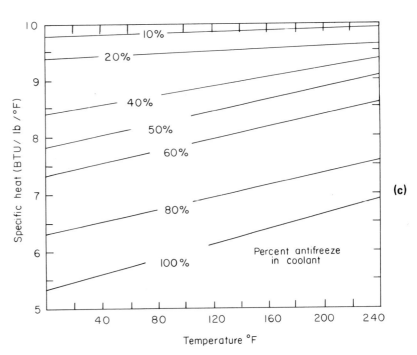

ials are added to keep the water from freezing. The first antifreezes were alcohol-based materials. These would boil away at the high operating temperatures encountered during some driving conditions. Alcohol-type antifreeze material has been replaced by glycol-based material that provides both antifreeze protection and has a high boiling temperature.

Glycol is unable to carry as much heat as water alone at the same temperature. As the percentage of glycol in water is increased, the freezing point of the mixture is lowered, the boiling point is raised, and the ability to carry heat is reduced. This occurs up to a concentration of 60% glycol. Additional glycol will cause the freezing point to reverse and increase. For best cooling system performance the glycol concentration should be no greater than that necessary to give the required freezing and boiling protection.

13-3 LIQUID COOLING SYSTEM DESIGN

Coolant enters the engine at the center of the inlet side of the pump. The coolant pump is a centrifugal pump; it pulls coolant in at the *impeller* center and discharges it at the impeller tips. The pump is sized and the impeller is designed to absorb no more power than necessary to provide adequate coolant flow. The coolant pump is driven by a belt from the crankshaft. The belt is tightened with an *idler*. On most engines, the alternator serves as the belt-tightening idler. As engine speeds increase, more heat is developed and more cooling capacity is required. The belt-driven pump increases the impeller speed as the engine speed increases to provide extra coolant flow at the very time it is needed.

Coolant leaving the pump impeller is fed through a *scroll*, a smoothly curved passage that changes the fluid flow direction with minimum loss in velocity. The scroll is connected to the front of the engine so it will direct the coolant into the engine block. On V engines, two outlets are used, one for each cylinder bank. Occasionally, diverters are necessary in the coolant pump scroll to equalize coolant flow between the cylinder banks for even cooling of the engine.

Coolant Flow in the Engine. Coolant may flow through the engine in two ways, parallel and series. In the parallel system, coolant flows into

Fig. 13-4 Typical location of the coolant pump.

Fig. 13-5 Coolant pump, impeller, and scroll.

the block under pressure, then crosses the gasket to the head through holes adjacent to each cylinder. In the series flow system, the coolant flows around all of the cylinders on each bank to the rear of the block where large passages allow the coolant to flow across the gasket to the rear of the heads. The coolant flows forward through the heads to an outlet at the highest point in the engine cooling passage located at the front of the engine. Some engines use a combination of these two systems and call it a series-parallel coolant flow.

The cooling passages inside the engine must be designed so that the whole system can be drained. It must also be designed so that there are no pockets in which steam can form. In series flow systems, bleed holes or steam slits in the gasket, block and head provide this function by short circuiting a very small amount of coolant. Often, this short-circuited coolant is directed to flow coolant on hot areas in the head, such as exhaust valves, spark plugs and the exhaust cross-over.

By-Pass. A thermostat is located at the engine outlet to restrict coolant flow until the en-

gine reaches the operating temperature of the thermostat. The cooling system is provided with a by-pass that allows a small part of the coolant to circulate within the engine during warmup while the thermostat is closed. The by-pass is a small passage that leads from the engine side of the thermostat to the inlet side of the coolant pump. Coolant will flow through the by-pass, short-circuiting the radiator anytime the coolant pressure is different on the ends of the by-pass, even if the thermostat is open. The by-pass may be cast or drilled into the engine and pump parts. This is called an *internal by-pass*. It may be an *external by-pass*, visible as a

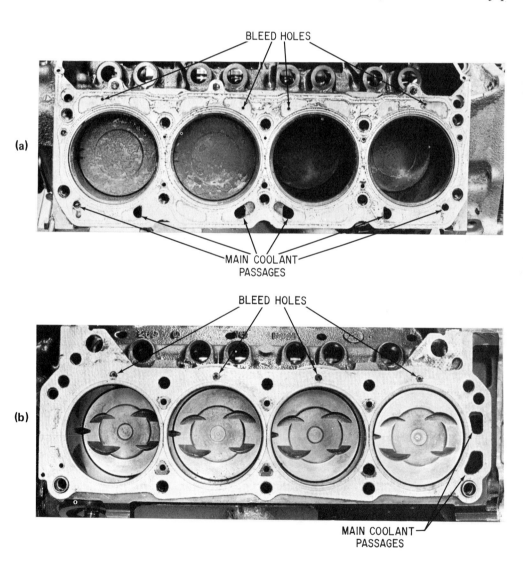

Fig. 13-6 Coolant flow types. (a) Parallel, (b) series.

(a)   (b)

Fig. 13-7 Coolant system bypass. (a) Internal, (b) external.

hose on the front of many engines, that connects the engine coolant outlet to the coolant pump. The by-pass aids in uniform warmup, eliminates hot spots and prevents excessive coolant pressure in the engine when the thermostat is closed.

Thermostat. The thermostat is a temperature-controlled valve placed at the engine coolant outlet. An encapsulated wax-based plastic pellet or aneroid bellows positioned on the engine side of the thermostatic valve is linked to the valve. As the engine warms, heat swells the pellet or bellows, opening the thermostat valve through a mechanical link. As the thermostat opens, it allows some coolant to flow to the radiator to be cooled while the remaining portion of the coolant continues to flow through the by-pass. This partial opening varies according to the engine cooling requirements that are needed to maintain normal engine temperatures. The coolant pump provides the force that causes coolant to flow through the cooling system. This flow is restricted by a closed thermostat and, therefore, the flow rate is low. The thermostat restriction causes the cooling system

pressure to rise. As the thermostat gradually opens, coolant flow rate increases and its pressure lowers. The thermostat will be wide open with maximum coolant flow only under extreme heat conditions, such as idling in traffic, or pulling a load up a long, steep grade in warm weather.

Radiator. The engine coolant outlet is connected to the top of the radiator by hoses and clamps. Within the radiator the coolant moves from the top to the bottom of the radiator as it cools. It leaves the lower radiator tank through an outlet and hose, going into the inlet side of the pump where it is recirculated through the engine.

Much of the cooling system capacity is based on the function of the radiator. Radiators are designed to obtain the maximum rate of heat transfer using minimum material and size to keep cost as low as possible. Vehicle designs also dictate available radiator space, and consequently, affect radiator design.

Two types of radiator cores are in common use in domestic automobiles, the serpentine fin core and the plate fin core. In each of these types,

Fig. 13-8 Typical automotive coolant system thermostats.

Fig. 13-9 Radiator and hoses.

coolant flows through oval-shaped tubes. Heat transfers through the tube wall and soldered points to the radiator fins. The fins are exposed to an air flow which removes heat and carries it away from the radiator.

Most automobile radiators are made from yellow brass or from copper. These materials are corrosion resistant, have good heat transfer ability, are easily formed, have the required strength characteristics, and are easily repaired by soldering. Some applications have used corrosion-protected steel; however, steel is seldom used in automobile radiators. Aluminum is used for radiators in special applications where weight is critical.

Core tubes are made from .0045" to .012" (.134 to .348 mm) sheet brass, using the thinnest possible materials for each application. They are rolled into round tubes and the joints sealed with a locking seam. The tubes are then coated with solder, compressed into an oval shape and cut to length. Fins are formed from .003" to .005" (.0762 to .127 mm) copper or brass, again using the thinnest possible material to save weight and cost.

(a)

(b)

Fig. 13-10 Radiator core types (Modine Manufacturing Company). (a) Serpentine, (b) plate type.

Serpentine fins are formed, stacked between the tubes, and held in a fixture. These assemblies are heated in an oven to fuse the joints and then the assembly is submerged in liquid solder. Capillary action pulls solder into the joints, assuring a tight joint that will readily transfer heat. The serpentine type is usually used in passenger cars. It is the least expensive of the two types and cools as well as the plate type. The serpentine type is held together with the soldered joint alone, while the plate type is mechanically held by the plate fins as well as solder. Plate-type cores are, therefore, stronger than the serpentine cores.

The main limitation to heat transfer in a radiator is on the air side. Heat transfers from the water to the fins as much as seven times faster than the heat transfers from the fins to the air, assuming equal surface exposure. The radiator's heat transfer capacity is the result of the number of fins per inch, the radiator height, width, and thickness, and the number of coolant tubes. The core must be capable of dissipating heat energy approximately equal to the power produced by the engine. Each horsepower is equivalent to 42.4 BTU per minute. As the engine power is increased, the heat dissipation requirement is also increased.

Coolant tubes are straight, free flowing tubes. The fins are often given a pattern to break up any smooth layer air flow that would insulate their surface. This turbulent flow will increase heat transfer rate, but will also add air resistance. Care is taken to design a radiator that will provide maximum cooling with minimum air resistance. With a given face area, radiator capacity may be increased by increasing the core thickness, packing more material into the same volume or both. Its capacity may also be increased by placing a shroud around the fan so more air will be pulled through the radiator.

Radiator headers and tanks that close off the ends of the core are made of sheet brass .020" to .050" (.051 to .127 mm) thick. These are fitted with tubular brass hose necks. The supporting sides are usually steel. The filler neck and the drain boss are brass. When a transmission oil cooler is used in the radiator, it is placed in the outlet tank where the coolant has the lowest temperature.

Radiators may be of the down flow or cross flow designs. In down flow designs, hot coolant from the engine is delivered to the top radiator

Fig. 13-11 Down flow radiator (The Dow Chemical Company).

Fig. 13-12 Cross flow radiator (Modine Manufacturing Company).

tank and cool coolant removed from the bottom. In cross flow designs, hot coolant goes to a tank on one side of the radiator and flows across the radiator through the coolant tubes to the tank on the other side. In the down flow designs, the coolant reserve tank is located on the top, or inlet side. In the cross flow design, the reserve tank is placed on the outlet side. Neither type is more or less efficient than the other. Available space generally dictates the choice of the two designs.

Pressure Cap. The filler neck is fitted with a pressure cap. The cap has a spring-loaded valve that will allow cooling system pressure to build up to the cap pressure setting, and then will release the excess pressure to prevent system damage.

Excess pressure usually forces some coolant from the system through an overflow. The overflow is a tube leading out below the radiator where coolant is lost. Some systems connect the overflow to a plastic container where excess coolant is held while the system is hot. When the system cools, the pressure is reduced and coolant is pulled back into the cooling system, keeping the system full. The cap used on a coolant system without a coolant saver is fitted with a vacuum valve that allows air to re-enter the system as the system cools, so that the radiator parts will not collapse under a vacuum. SAE standard latching notches on the cap and neck are sized so that a high-pressure cap will not fit a low-pressure system.

Automobile engines are pressurized to raise the boiling temperature of the coolant. The boil-

ing temperature of the coolant will increase approximately 3°F (1.6°C) for each pound increase in pressure. Under standard atmospheric pressure a 50% glycol mixture will boil at 229°F (110°C). With a 15-pound (6.8 kg) pressure cap, this mixture would boil at 274°F (135°C), which is a maximum engine temperature even for the lubricating system. This high coolant system pressure serves two functions. First, it allows the engine to run close to 200°F (93.3°C) with no danger of boiling coolant; second, the higher the operating temperature of the coolant, the more heat it can transfer. The heat transferred by the cooling system is proportional to the temperature difference between the coolant and the outside air. This characteristic has led to small high pressure radiator designs that are capable of handling large quantities of heat. It can be seen that for proper cooling, it is imperative to have the right pressure cap correctly installed.

A problem that sometimes occurs under these conditions involves the coolant pump. For the pump to function, the inlet side of the pump must

Fig. 13-13 Cooling system with a plastic overflow container to conserve coolant.

Fig. 13-14 Pressure cap with the vacuum valve held open.

Fig. 13-15 Coolant pump belt drive.

have a lower pressure than its outlet side. If inlet pressure is lowered too much, the coolant at the pump inlet could boil, producing vapor. The pump will then spin the coolant vapors and not pump coolant, thus causing the engine to overheat. This condition is called pump *cavitation.*

Fan. Air is forced across the radiator core by a cooling fan which is usually attached to a hub on the coolant pump shaft. The fan is designed to cool the engine coolant at the lowest fan speed when the engine is operating at its highest coolant temperature. The fan is sometimes *shrouded* to increase the cooling system efficiency. The horsepower required to drive the fan increases much faster than the fan speed increases. Higher fan speed increases the fan noise level as well. Thermoregulating and viscous-drive fans have been developed to drive the fan only as fast as required to cool the engine coolant and to limit maximum fan speed. This reduces the fan power requirements and fan noise.

Extra Heat Loads. Cooling systems have an added heat load when air conditioning is used. The

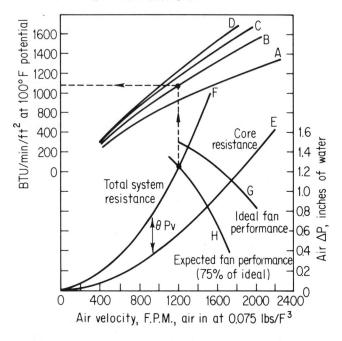

Radiator core performance
Water flow per foot of core width:
    A – 10.2 GPM (0.69 fl/sec through tubes)
    B – 20.3 GPM (1.39 fl/sec through tubes)
    C – 30.5 GPM (2.08 fl/sec through tubes)
    D – 50.8 GPM (3.47 fl/sec through tubes)
    D – Above 50.8 GPM

Fig. 13-16 Performance curves of a typical radiator (Modine Manufacturing Company).

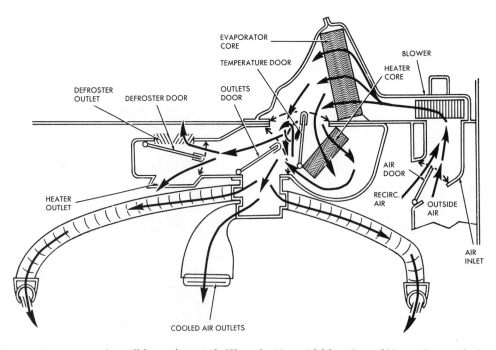

Fig. 13-17 Heater-air conditioner air controls (Chevrolet Motor Division, General Motors Corporation).

high-temperature air conditioning condenser is usually located in front of the radiator and this raises the incoming air temperature 10°F to 20°F (5.5°C to 11°C). Air-conditioned cars are therefore equipped with a larger capacity radiator and a higher capacity fan than cars without air conditioning. High-capacity cooling systems are also used on cars equipped for trailer towing.

Spark-retarded emission controls increase the amount of heat transferred to the cooling system. There may be as much as 25% additional heat transferred at idle. In traffic, the additional heat needing to be transferred may become critical. To help relieve this critical situation, manufacturers equip many engines with a temperature-sensing vacuum valve. When the coolant reaches a critical temperature, engine vacuum is used to advance the ignition timing with the distributor vacuum-advance unit.

This temporarily improves combustion, but reduces emission control; however, it lowers the heat transfer rate and increases engine speed with an accompanying increase in coolant pump and fan speed so the engine does not become damaged by overheat.

Most of the heat absorbed from the engine by the cooling system is wasted energy. Some of this heat, however, is recovered by the vehicle heater. Warm coolant is bypassed through the core tubes of the heater. Air is passed through the heater fins where it is warmed. It is then sent to the passenger compartment. In some vehicles, the heater and air conditioner work in series to maintain a constant vehicle compartment temperature.

REVIEW QUESTIONS

1. Name two types of cooling systems.

2. Why is it undesirable to use excess antifreeze?

3. What kind of coolant pump is used?

4. Where does coolant enter the pump?

5. When is the function of a cooling system bypassed?

6. Where does a cooling system bypass the coolant?

7. When is the by-pass most useful?

8. When is coolant system temperature the highest?

9. What valves are built into the pressure cap?

10. What is the value of using glycol coolant in a pressurized cooling system?

11. Where is pressure the highest in an operating cooling system?

12. Where is pressure the lowest in an operating cooling system?

13. What device makes use of some of the heat normally expelled from the engine radiator?

14

Cooling System Service

The cooling system is one of the most maintenance free systems in the entire engine. Normal maintenance involves an occasional check on the coolant level. Normal maintenance should also include a visual inspection for signs of coolant system leaks and for the condition of the coolant hoses and fan drive belts at the same time.

The coolant level should only be checked when the engine is cool. Removing the pressure cap from a hot engine will relieve the cooling system pressure while the coolant temperature is above its atmospheric boiling temperature. When the cap is removed the pressure will drop to atmospheric pressure, causing the coolant to boil instantly. This forces coolant from the system. Coolant will be lost and someone may be injured or burned by the high temperature coolant that boils out of the filler opening.

The antifreeze is renewed at periodic intervals. When the coolant system is empty during the coolant change is a good time to replace hoses and to check thermostats. Fan drive belts can then be replaced without draining the coolant.

Coolant system problems are indicated by leaks, excessive engine temperature, and by low engine temperature. The cause of a problem is primarily determined by knowledge of the operation of a cooling system and a good visual inspection. This is supplemented by tests to determine the coolant temperature and coolant pressure.

14-1 DRAIN AND REFILL

Manufacturers recommend that a cooling system be flushed and that the antifreeze be replaced at specified intervals. Some recommend yearly antifreeze replacement, while others recommend replacement every two years. If the engine is cool there is no chance of being injured by draining hot coolant. The radiator is drained by opening a petcock in the bottom tank and the block is drained by opening plugs or petcocks located in the lower part of the cooling passage, one on an inline engine and two on V engines, one on each side.

When the coolant is out of the engine, it is a good time to do preventive maintenance such as replacing hoses and checking the thermostat. Flushing is also a good preventive maintenance practice. Water should be run into the filler opening with the drains remaining open. It should be allowed to run until only clear water comes from the system. In some cases the drains are closed and the radiator is filled with water that has a flushing solution added. After a short run to thoroughly circulate the solution, it is drained and the system flushed with water.

The volume of the cooling system should be checked in the owner's handbook or engine service manual. The cooling system volume is noted on a chart that comes with the antifreeze to determine the antifreeze quantity needed for the protection

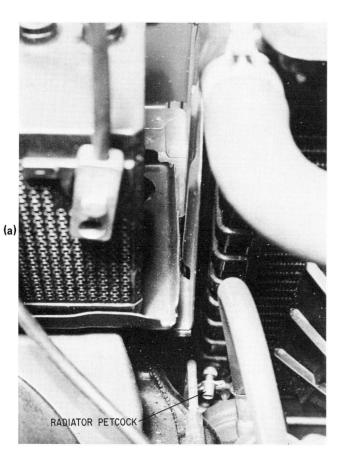

(a)

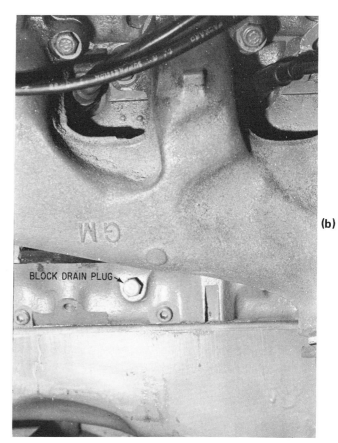

(b)

BLOCK DRAIN PLUG

RADIATOR PETCOCK

Fig. 14-1 Coolant system drains. (a) Radiator petcock, (b) block drain plug.

desired. Protection is required against freezing and against boiling. On automobiles with factory air conditioning the antifreeze keeps the coolant from freezing in the heater core during maximum cooling. The correct amount of antifreeze is put into the radiator followed by enough water to completely fill the system. In most systems small air pockets can occur, so the engine must be thoroughly warmed to open the thermostat so that full coolant flow can occur. The heater must also be turned on. In some cases it is necessary to slightly loosen the upper heater hose to release trapped air in the heater. After the engine has been thoroughly warmed and allowed to cool, the system should be topped off with water to complete the refill job.

14-2 HOSES

Coolant system hoses are critical to engine cooling. As the hoses get old they become soft or brittle and sometimes swell, depending upon their material and the engine service conditions. If a hose breaks while in service all coolant will be lost. A hose

Fig. 14-2 Coolant hoses.

should be replaced anytime it appears to be ab-normal. It is good preventive maintenance to re-place hoses at regular periods, such as every two years.

When hoses require replacement the coolant must be drained. If the same coolant is to be rein-stalled in the engine it will have to be caught in a drain pan. If the coolant is to be replaced the old coolant can be dumped into a waste drain. It is only necessary to drain coolant from the petcock located at the bottom of the radiator to remove sufficient coolant for hose removal. Hose clamps are loosened and slipped off the portion of the hose that is on the hose neck. Two types of hose clamps are commonly found on coolant hoses, a wire spring clamp and a band tightened with a screw. The wire spring clamp-type is easily removed and replaced with special pliers. Common slip-jaw pliers can be used, but it is much more difficult to keep them from slipping from the clamp. The band-type clamp can be removed and installed using only

a screwdriver. The hose can then be worked free from the hose neck; care should be taken to avoid bending the hose neck on the radiator. The hose neck should be cleaned and a new hose slipped in place, so that the hose is fully inserted over the neck. Hose clamps are secured over the hose at a point from 1/4 to 1/2 in. (6.35 to 12.7 mm) from the end of the hose. If the clamp is too close to the hose end it may slip off. If it is placed too far on-to the hose the edge of the hose may curl and cause a leak. When the hoses are in place and the drain petcock is closed, the cooling system can be re-filled. After the engine has been warmed the cool-ant system should be topped off with additional coolant.

14-3 THERMOSTAT

An overheating engine may result from a faulty thermostat. An engine that does not get warm enough always indicates a faulty thermostat. The thermostat is located in a housing on the engine outlet near the top front of the engine. The thermo-stat must be removed to check its correct operation.

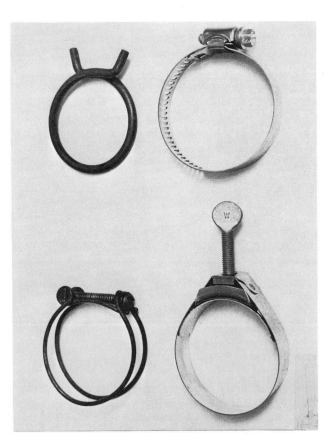

Fig. 14-3 Hose clamp types used on coolant system hoses.

Fig. 14-4 Checking a thermostat's opening temperature.

Coolant will have to be drained from the radiator drain petcock to lower the coolant level below the thermostat. The upper hose is removed from the thermostat housing neck, then the housing is removed to expose the thermostat. If the engine operates cold the thermostat will be stuck open. If the thermostat is closed, a 0.015 in. (0.39 mm) feeler gauge should be forced in the opening so that the thermostat hangs on the feeler gauge. The thermostat is then suspended by the feeler gauge in a bath along with a thermometer. The bath is heated until the thermostat opens enough to release and fall from the feeler gauge. This is the opening temperature of the thermostat. If it is the same temperature as the one stamped on the thermostat it will be satisfactory for use. If it is not, the thermostat should be replaced.

The gasket flanges of the engine and thermostat housing are cleaned and coated with gasket sealer. The thermostat is placed in the engine with the sensing portion toward the engine. The housing is fitted in place with a new gasket and carefully seated to assure proper thermostat positioning. The neck cap screw threads are coated with gasket sealer and tightened in place. Then the upper hose is installed and the system is refilled.

14-4 CLEANING

Overheating problems may be caused by deposits that restrict coolant flow. These can often be loosened by *back flushing*. Back flushing requires the use of a special gun that mixes air with water at a pressure low enough that it will not damage the cooling system. The upper radiator hose is removed from the radiator and the lower hose is removed from the engine. Heater hoses should be removed and the openings plugged. The gun is fitted into the lower hose so that the radiator flushes upward. A long upper hose can be attached to deflect the flushing water from the engine. Deposits will come out of the filler opening and out of the upper hose neck. The engine block is back flushed by fitting the gun into the upper hose (the thermostat and lower hose must be removed) and forcing the air and water mixture backward through the engine. If after flushing some deposits still plug the inner portion of the radiator core, the radiator will have to be removed and sent to a radiator repair shop for a thorough cleaning. After cleaning, the radiator is reinstalled, along with the thermostat; hoses; and drains, plugs, or petcocks. Then the system is filled with coolant.

Overheating can also result from exterior

Fig. 14-5 Checking the coolant's antifreeze concentration.

radiator plugging caused by dirt and insects. This type of plugging can be seen if the technician looks straight through the radiator while a light is behind it. It can usually be cleaned with water pressure from a hose applied to the engine side of the radiator. The water should flow freely through the core at all locations. If it does not, continued use of water pressure and some air pressure will usually loosen the material that is plugging the core. If this does not clean the core, the radiator should be removed for a thorough cleaning. Prodding with a wire may rupture the thin tubes that carry coolant so that the radiator will have to be repaired.

14-5 THERMAL FAN

The fan is driven by a belt from the crankshaft. It turns faster as the engine turns faster. Generally speaking, the engine is required to produce more power at higher speeds and it will also transfer more heat. Increased fan speed aids in the cooling that is required. Engine heat is also critical at low engine

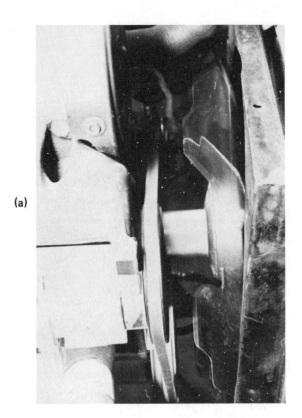 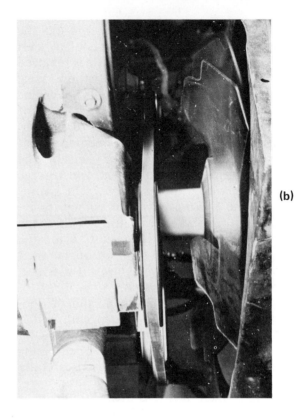

Fig. 14-6 Fan with flexible blades. (a) Engine operating at low speed, (b) engine operating at high speed. Photographs were taken with a high speed flash.

speeds in traffic. The vehicle moves slowly and the fan turns slowly and so the engine cooling capacity is insufficient under these conditions. Air conditioning may add an additional heat load to the system. Thermal fans have been developed with smaller drive pulleys that will turn the fan faster for better radiator cooling during low engine speed operation. Thermal fan regulation is designed to avoid excessive cooling at high engine speeds and to minimize power absorption and noise.

The simplest type of thermal fan is one made with flexible blades. At low speeds the blades have a high angle that pulls large quantities of air. At higher engine speeds the flexible blades flatten, primarily by centrifugal force, so the fan pulls less air during each revolution.

A second type of thermal fan has a silicone coupling type fan drive mounted between the drive pulley and the fan that will allow slippage when fan loads become great at high engine speeds. At low engine speeds it functions without slippage. The coupling will drive the fan as engine speeds increase until fan loads become high enough to cause slippage. Increases in engine speed above this point will not increase fan speed.

A third type of thermal fan has a thermostatic spring added to the silicone coupling fan drive. The

Fig. 14-7 Fan with a silicone drive operating within a fan shroud.

174

(a)

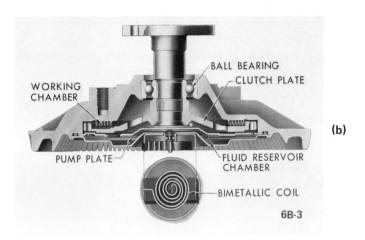

(b)

Fig. 14-8 Thermal fan drives. (a) Silicone drive coupling on the left with thermostatic spring valves in the center and right drive couplings, (b) section view of a thermal drive (Buick Motor Division, General Motors Corporation).

thermostatic spring operates a valve that allows the fan to freewheel when the radiator is cold. As the radiator warms to about 150°F (65°C) the air hitting the thermostatic spring will cause the spring to change its shape. This will open a valve that allows the drive to operate like the silicone coupling drive. When the engine is very cold the fan may operate at high speeds for a short time until the drive fluid warms slightly, then the fan speed will drop to idle.

In some small import automobiles the cooling fan drive is with an electric motor. Temperature switches in the electric motor circuit prevent fan operation when the engine is cold. As the engine warms the fan begins to run at a speed that provides required cooling.

When all other conditions are checked, an overheating problem may result from an improperly operating thermal fan drive. This can be checked by a stroboscopic light, similar to a timing light, that will measure fan speeds under different engine operating conditions. Unfortunately, these stroboscopic lights are not usually available in the service shop. When a thermal fan drive malfunction is suspected the standard procedure in a typical service shop is to replace the drive coupling with a new one and try it out.

14-6 WATER PUMP

The fan is mounted on the water pump shaft so the pump speed is governed by the fan pulley size and engine speed. The rate of coolant flow through the system is therefore controlled by selecting the size

of the pump impeller to match the speed of the coolant pump to the cooling requirements of the engine. Replacement pumps must have the correct impeller for proper cooling system operation.

Three parts of the pump may cause trouble and lead to pump failure. Pump seal failure is the most common malfunction. The pump seal is a spring-loaded carbon-face seal that rides against a ceramic seal surface on the impeller. A bleed hole to the pump exterior is located between the seal and the shaft bearings to allow leaking coolant to run out of the engine before it can contaminate the pump shaft bearings.

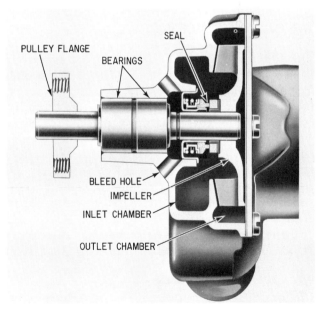

Fig. 14-9 Parts of a coolant pump (Chevrolet Motor Division, General Motors Corporation).

A second pump problem is impeller breakage or impeller slippage on the pump shaft. The impeller may be plastic, cast iron, cast aluminum, or stamped steel. A damaged impeller will not pump enough coolant through the system. The only way to be sure the impeller is satisfactory is to remove the pump and examine it visually. In some engines a pump cover will also have to be removed.

The third problem is the pump bearings. These are sealed for life. If they begin to get noisy they will have to be replaced with new bearings.

Many service manuals describe water pump overhaul procedures; however, parts departments seldom stock the required parts. The reason for this is that mechanics and technicians are seldom able to make the repairs satisfactorily with the tools and equipment normally available in the shop. The biggest problem in coolant pump rebuilding is that great care is required to make sure the pump shaft seal is installed properly. During manufacture the pumps are assembled in an air-conditioned "clean-room" at an exact assembled height to give the seal the correct preload. In spite of this care one will occasionally leak. The technician does not have much of a chance to make a satisfactory water pump repair in a typical service shop. It is a common service practice when a pump is faulty to purchase a new or factory-rebuilt pump rather than run the chance of a comeback coolant pump job.

14-7 RADIATOR SERVICE

Unless they are physically damaged, most radiators are serviced by keeping the radiator exterior and interior clean. Vibration will sometimes loosen some of the soldered joints. These can often be resoldered with the radiator in place, especially open joints that frequently occur around the tanks. Care must be exercised in soldering a radiator because the heat necessary to make a repair may loosen other soldered joints. In most cases it is advisable to take the radiator to a specialized radiator repair shop.

The radiator is easily removed. First the coolant is drained and the hoses are disconnected. If the radiator contains a transmission cooler these lines will also have to be disconnected from the radiator. The radiator is held in the vehicle with sheetmetal steel side supports or it is clamped in a rubber cushion. These must be unbolted to free

the radiator. The radiator can then be lifted from the vehicle. After repairs the radiator assembly is replaced in the reverse order.

14-8 TROUBLESHOOTING

One of the most common coolant system problems is a loss of coolant. Coolant can get out of the system through leaks and through an overflow pipe. Leaks are usually visible and can be detected after a thoroughly warm engine is turned off. Most systems are equipped with a pressure cap to limit maximum system pressure. As the coolant temperature increases the pressure increases. While the engine is operating, the coolant temperature is kept below maximum by coolant circulation and radiator cooling. When the hot engine is turned off, cylinder heat will transfer to the coolant that is not being circulated. This added heat raises the coolant system pressure. Leaks will be most apparent when this high pressure exists.

Sometimes coolant leaks can be located by placing a special cooling system pressure tester in place of the radiator cap. The system is pressurized to the cap pressure setting. If no leakage occurs the pressure will hold steady. If leakage occurs the pressure will fall. Leaks can usually be observed visually while this test pressure is on the cooling system.

Fig. 14-10 Pressure testing a cooling system.

Fig. 14-11 Coolant overflow reservoir.

Fig. 14-12 Testing a pressure cap.

Leaks can occur at the thermostat flange, at coolant hose joints, in the radiator, in the heater core, or in engine soft plugs. Any leak should be immediately repaired before loss of coolant causes the engine to overheat and does costly damage.

Coolant loss can occur as the coolant expands while it is being heated. This expanded coolant is forced out through the pressure cap and the overflow pipe. Some automobiles connect the overflow pipe with a plastic reservoir similar to the windshield washer fluid bottle. Hot coolant overflows into the bottle. When the coolant cools and contracts, the coolant is drawn back into the radiator from the reservoir to avoid loss. If the cap is defective on systems that do not have an overflow bottle, it can cause loss of coolant through the overflow. Caps are checked with a cooling system pressure tester that measures the cap release pressure. The cap should hold its design pressure without leakage. Faulty caps should be replaced.

Coolant overflow will also occur if combustion gases leak into the coolant system. This happens when the head gasket does not seal properly or when there is a crack in the head. Sometimes these internal engine leaks will allow coolant to enter the engine interior and mix with the motor oil. Internal leakage is usually indicated by an increase in oil quantity with a brown or white foamy appearance. Internal leaks should be corrected as soon as possible to minimize engine damage.

Combustion leakage and air leaking on the suction side of the pump can often be observed by filling the coolant system clear up into the filler neck. With the cap off and the engine running, leakage is indicated by bubbles forming in the coolant at the filler neck. Another method is to place the radiator pressure tester on the filler neck in place of the filler cap, then start the engine. Combustion or suction air leakage will cause pressure to rapidly increase in the system. If a hydrocarbon-carbon monoxide tester is available combustion leakage will be indicated by hydrocarbons at the filler neck when the tester pickup is held above the coolant.

The coolant pump, as well as the fan, is driven by a belt. Belts, like hoses, deteriorate. They stretch, wear, and crack. These conditions can be checked visually. A loose belt will slip and will not drive the pump or fan at the speed required for proper cooling. Belt tension is critical for correct performance. A tension gauge will provide the best method of adjusting belt tension. In some installations a square hole is provided in the idler bracket so a torque wrench can be used to adjust tension. Other methods used to adjust tension are not reliable.

If the belt breaks the pump stops turning and will not force coolant flow. This allows the engine to overheat. In many automobiles the same belt that drives the fan and water pump also drives the

alternator, so when it breaks the alternator stops charging. This gives the driver an immediate visual notice of failure. It is advisable to examine the belts frequently and to replace them at regular periods, just as hoses are replaced, to provide trouble-free service.

As hoses become old they may become soft. If the lower hose is soft, it may collapse because of coolant pump suction. The collapsed hose restricts coolant flow, causing the engine to overheat. A properly maintained cooling system will give the engine a long trouble-free service life.

Fig. 14-13 One type of gauge used to check belt tension.

REVIEW QUESTIONS

1. When should the coolant level on an engine be checked?

2. Where are the coolant system drains located?

3. How can the technician determine that the engine cooling system has been adequately flushed when renewing the coolant?

4. When should a coolant hose be replaced?

5. Which condition directly indicates a faulty thermostat—an abnormally cool running engine or an abnormally hot running engine?

6. What procedure is used to clean the interior of the cooling system?

7. How should the exterior of the radiator be cleaned?

8. What is the purpose of a thermal fan?

9. What is the recommended way to service a leaking water pump?

10. What is the most common coolant system problem?

APPENDICES

APPENDICES

A

Glossary

A

Abnormal Combustion. Completion of combustion faster than normal as a result of surface ignition or detonation.

Abrasive. A rough material that will cut or scratch a moving surface.

Accessory. A device that performs a secondary function.

Actuate. To move or produce movement.

Adhesion. The characteristic that causes one material to stick to or cling to another.

After Market. The sales market designed for the consumer after he purchases a product from the dealer.

Ambient Temperature. The temperature of the surrounding air.

Annulus. An outer ring or space between an object and the outer edge of a hole.

Apex. The point of a triangular shaped object.

Atmospheric Pressure. The surrounding air pressure produced by the total weight of the atmosphere.

Atom. The smallest particle of an element. Made of protons, neutrons, and electrons.

Atomize. To break into very fine particles, such as fuel delivery by a discharge nozzle.

Available Voltage. Maximum voltage that an ignition system is capable of producing.

B

Barrel. The opening in a carburetor through which the air/fuel mixture enters the manifold.

Battery Post. The terminal of the battery on which electrical cables are attached.

Bead. A ridge around the edge of a part.

Bell Crank. A moving arm that pivots near the middle. It is used to change the direction of motion.

Bimetallic Spring. A spring made of a double strip of two different metals. When it is heated or cooled it will bend.

Block. The large casting that forms the engine base.

Bog. An expression used to describe an engine misfiring condition that occurs as the throttle is opened. The engine power drops rather than increases.

Bore. The diameter of a hole. The carburetor opening often called a barrel.

Boss. A heavy cast section that is used for support, such as the heavy section around a bearing.

Bowl. A compartment in a carburetor containing a specified level of gasoline.

Bumping. Very short snaps of the starter switch that will turn the engine slightly with each snap. It is used to position the crankshaft for timing.

Bypass. To go around some restriction such as a thermostat, valve, switch, circuit, etc.

C

Cam. A raised or flattened section on a rotating cylinder or disc that is used to provide a timed mechanical movement.

Cap. A cover.

Canister. An enclosed can containing activated charcoal or carbon. Used in the evaporative emission-control system to absorb unburned hydrocarbon vapors when the engine is not running.

Cavitation. A space created at the center of a rotating pump when it does not fill as fast as the fluid is pumped out.

Chamber. An enclosed volume.

Check Valve. A valve that will allow flow in one direction and will stop flow in the opposite direction.

Cluster. A number of devices or items grouped together. Carburetor jetting placed in one part.

Compensation. The system in the main circuit of a carburetor that prevents an overrich mixture at high air velocities through the venturi.

Condense. Liquid separating from vapor as the vapor is cooled.

Contact Set. The breaker points that interrupt the ignition system primary circuit to produce a spark at the spark plug.

Corrosion. A combination of a metal and oxygen or water that causes the surface of the metal to disappear.

Cubic Inch Displacement. The volume swept by the pistons as the crankshaft rotates one revolution.

Cycle. A complete circle back to the beginning. In engines, a series of events; intake, compression, power, and exhaust.

D

Damper. A plate on a shaft within a passage. As the shaft is rotated the plate opens or closes the passage.

Deposits. Material remaining after an activity, such as the material that coats the intake manifold after the fuel evaporates or the material that accumulates on the inner surface of the exhaust pipe.

Depression. A lower value. Air pressure below atmospheric pressure that is called vacuum in the automotive service trade.

Dew Point. The temperature at which condensation occurs while a vapor is being cooled.

Diagnose. To determine the cause of a malfunction through analysis of data from test equipment, troubleshooting charts, and knowledge about the operation of the system.

Dieseling. A name used for engine run on after a hot engine is turned off. The ignition of the charge is the result of hot spots in the combustion chamber.

Differential Pressure. Differences in pressure that cause flow from the highest pressure to the lowest pressure.

Distort. To twist, bend, or buckle.

Divert. To change the direction of flow.

Drivability. Smooth engine operation at all vehicle speeds.

Drop Out. The separation of heavy components from the flow of a light fluid.

E

Eccentric. A circle superimposed on a second circle with each circle having a different center.

Elastomer. A rubber-like plastic or synthetic material.

Emission. Gaseous material expelled, usually referring to harmful gases being expelled from an engine.

Erosion. The process of wearing away by high velocity abrasive particles.

Evaporation. Conversion of a liquid to a vapor.

F

Filter. A device to remove particles from a fluid.

Float. A device supported by fluid, as a carburetor float used to sense fluid level.

Flood. An air/fuel mixture too rich to ignite.

Flow Chart. A step-by-step procedure used in troubleshooting.

Flush. Wash off.

H

Hair Spring. A very fine spring coiled in a flat plane so the diameter of the spring keeps expanding as it is wound.

Heat Riser. A valve in the exhaust that directs exhaust gases against the outer surface of the intake manifold below the carburetor when the engine is cold.

Humidity. Water vapor in the air.

Hydrometer. A floating device that measures specific gravity of a fluid by the depth the float sinks into the fluid.

I

Idle. Running freely with no load or power being transmitted; with engines, the lowest no-load speed.

Impeller. A rotating part that increases the moving speed or velocity of a fluid.

J

Jet. A carefully sized opening in a carburetor passage to measure the flow of either gasoline or air.

L

Limiter. A device in a carburetor that prevents excessively rich air/fuel mixtures at idle.

Lobe. The high portion of a cam.

Malfunction. A fault or improper operation.

Manifold. Cast passages that connect openings from each cylinder to a common opening.

Mass. The amount of material. Often equated to weight for easy understanding.

Mean Effective Pressure. The calculated average pressure in the combustion chamber during the power stroke.

Mechanic. A person who services mechanical devices.

Misfire. Partial or intermittent nonfiring of one cylinder on a running engine.

N

Nipple. A hollow metal connection point on which a hose is attached.

Normally Closed. A switch or valve that is closed in its static non-operating position.

Normally Open. A switch or valve that is open in its non-operating static position.

Nozzle. A hollow part through which a fluid flows or sprays into a gas.

O

Offset. A part with the center of each end parallel but not in line with the other.

Owner's Handbook. A book supplied with each new automobile that describes the features of the automobile and the recommended maintenance schedule.

Oxidation. The chemical combination of a metal with oxygen.

P

Part Throttle. Engine operating speed between idle and full throttle. Generally considered to be cruising speed.

Passage. A tubular shaped opening through which a liquid or gas can flow.

PCV. Positive crankcase ventilation that draws air through the crankcase of a running engine.

Percolate. To force a liquid up a passage by means of an expansion of gases below the liquid.

Points. The contact breaker that interrupts the primary ignition circuit.

Pontoon. A container or block that will float on a liquid to support an object.

Port. An opening through which liquids or gases flow.

Power. The amount of work done in a specific period of time. One horsepower equals 33,000 ft lb per min (745.7 watts and 42.4 BTU per min).

Preflame. The gases ahead of the flame front during combustion.

Pressure. A force on a surface area.

Push Rod. The rod between the cam and rocker arm that moves the rocker arm.

R

Ramp. A gradual slope or incline on a cam to take up clearance or lash.

Rate. A quantity of one thing measured in terms of quantity of a different thing.

Read Out. An observed instrument reading.

Remote. Operated from some distance.

Road Load. A load applied to an engine that simulates the engine load required for cruising speed.

Rocker Arm. An arm that when moved at one end pivots around a point to produce a movement on the opposite end in the opposite direction.

Roll. A term used to describe an engine idling with a very rich mixture that causes the engine to increase and decrease speed.

Rotor. The part of a distributor that directs the secondary voltage to the proper spark plug cable.

S

Sag. Engine power loss during acceleration as the result of improper air/fuel mixture ratios.

Scroll. A curved passage that becomes larger and has an increasing radius as it curves.

Seal. A device that prevents leakage between two objects.

Secondary. The high voltage side of the ignition system. The carburetor barrel that opens to provide maximum air flow through a carburetor.

Series. A single path through a number of items, one after the other.

Service Manual. A paperback book produced by the automobile manufacturer each year that shows the correct servicing procedures.

Set Screw. A screw in the side of a member on a shaft. The screw is tightened or set against the shaft to prevent movement between the member and shaft.

Shroud. A cover between the edges of the radiator and the fan tip. Used to increase the efficiency of the fan.

Shunt. A device that produces a by-pass function.

Signal. Changing pressures in a carburetor that produces a change in air or fuel metering.

Siphon. A passage that runs up from one opening located below a liquid in a chamber and then on to the other opening located outside and below the chamber through which the liquid will automatically pass.

Soft Plug. An expandable cap that is used to close a machined opening in a casting.

Spherical. A ball or sphere shape.

Stall. Unintentional engine stoppage.

Step. An abrupt change in cam shape.

Stoichiometric. A chemically balanced air/fuel mixture that provides complete combustion.

Stress. A force placed on a part.

Stroke. Piston movement from one extreme limit to the other.

Stumble. A momentary misfiring at the beginning of acceleration.

Suction. Lowering pressure so that there is a flow toward the lowered pressure.

Sump. The lowest part of an engine crankcase.

Surface Tension. The interaction of the molecules on the surface of a liquid that causes them to act as a surface skin.

T

Tab. A short projection on a part.

Tang. A lip or projection from a surface.

Technician. A specialist in the technical details of automotive service.

Temperature Compensation. A device that changes operating conditions as the temperature changes.

Test Light. A light used to check electrical continuity or voltage.

Thermostat. A device used to maintain constant temperature.

Thermostatic Arm. An arm that changes its angle as the temperature changes.

Timing. The number of crankshaft degrees from the piston top center when the ignition starts combustion.

Torque. The twisting force on a shaft in lb-ft.

Turbulence. Irregular swirling currents within a liquid or gas.

V

Vacuum. A pressure less than atmospheric.

Vaporize. To convert from the liquid state to the vapor state.

Vent. A passage that allows pressure to escape.

Venturi. A smooth flowing restriction in the carburetor that increases air velocity to lower its pressure.

Viscosity. The thickness or fluid body of a liquid.

Volatility. The tendency to evaporate.

W

Warpage. A twist or bend out of the original form.

Abbreviations for Emission-Control Components and Systems

AG	Air guard		EGR	Exhaust gas recirculation
AIR	Air injection reactor		ELC	Evaporative loss control
AIS	Air injection system		ESC	Electronic spark control
BCDD	Boost-controlled deceleration device		FDC	Fuel decel system
BPT	Back pressure transducer		FDV	Fuel decel valve
BPV	Back pressure transducer valve		FEC	Fuel evaporation control
			FID	Flame ionization detector
CAP	Clean air package		FTVC	Fuel tank vapor control
CAS	Clean air system		FVR	Fuel vapor recovery
CCEGR	Coolant controlled exhaust gas recirculation			
CCIE	Coolant controlled idle enrichment		HAI	Heated air inlet
CCS	Controlled combustion system		HC	Hydrocarbon
CCV	Closed crankcase ventilation		HCV	Heat control valve
CEC	Combined emission control		HEI	High energy ignition
CO	Carbon monoxide			
COVAC	Combined vacuum system		IFC	Integrated fuel control
CSC	Coolant spark control		IMCO	Improved combustion
CSSA	Cold start spark advance			
CTAV	Cold temperature activated vacuum		NIDR	Nondispersive infrared analyzer
CTO	Coolant temperature override		NO_x	Oxides of nitrogen
DMS	Distributor modulator system		OSAC	Orifice spark advance control
DVB	Delayed vacuum by-pass			
DVV	Distributor vacuum valve		PCV	Positive crankcase ventilation
			PGM	Platinum group metal
ECS	Evaporative control system		PTC	Positive temperature coefficient heater
EDM	Electronic distributor modulator		PVA	Ported vacuum advance
EEC	Exhaust emission control		PVS	Ported vacuum switch
EECS	Evaporative emission-control system			
EER	Exhaust emission reduction		SDV	Spark delay valve
EFE	Early fuel evaporation		SPTC	Spark timing control

Abbreviations

SCS	Speed control switch
TAC	Thermostatically controlled air cleaner
TAV	Temperature activated vacuum
TCS	Transmission controlled spark
TIC	Thermal ignition control valve
TOC	Throttle opener control
TRS	Transmission regulated spark
TSP	Throttle solenoid positioner
TVS	Thermostatic vacuum switch
VACV	Vacuum-advance control valve
VBV	Vacuum bias valve
VDV	Vacuum differential valve
VRV	Vacuum reducer valve
VVA	Venturi vacuum amplifier

INDEX

Index